Jeff Galloway

100 Reasons to Run . . . NOW!

How to Jumpstart Your Run

Meyer & Meyer Sport

British Library Cataloguing in Publication Data
A catalogue record for this book is available from the British Library

Jeff Galloway
100 Reasons to Run . . . NOW!
How to Jumpstart your Run
Maidenhead: Meyer & Meyer Sport (UK) Ltd., 2012
ISBN 978-1-84126-345-8

© 2012 Meyer & Meyer Sport (UK) Ltd.
Auckland, Beirut, Budapest, Cairo, Cape Town, Dubai, Indianapolis,
Kindberg, Maidenhead, Sydney, Olten, Singapore, Tehran, Toronto
Member of the World
Sport Publishers' Association (WSPA)
www.w-s-p-a.org
Printed and bound by: B.O.S.S Druck und Medien GmbH, Germany
ISBN 978-1-84126-345-8
E-Mail: info@m-m-sports.com
www.m-m-sports.com

Contents

© Galina Barskaya/iStockphoto/Thinkstock

Introduction:
You never know
what talents are hidden inside

Like many children in Navy families, I attended 13 schools by the time I finished the 7th grade. At this point, my father became a teacher, we moved to Atlanta, and my new school required each boy to work out with an athletic team after school every day. Because of the moves, I had avoided sports and exercise, did not have sports skills, had become lazy and had gained a lot of weight.

My patchwork of educational experiences had not prepared me for the demanding and competitive academic environment at this Prep school, and I was struggling. The principal's comment on the report card was: "A little more of a push next year and Jeff will make the top half of the class." I was already studying more hours every week than most of the students I knew, who were scoring better on tests. I believed that I was intellectually inferior.

During the fall, I tried football, which was a total disaster from my and my coaches' perspective. Before choosing a sport for the next quarter, I asked several of the other lazy kids for their choices and was surprised to hear that many had chosen Winter Track Conditioning. The consensus among the slackers was that the track coach was the most lenient in the school. "Tell him you are running on the trails, and you only have to jog 200 yards to the woods and hide out."

I did just that for two days. On the third day, an older athlete I liked, looked at me and said "Galloway, you're running with us today." I quickly came up with my strategy: as we entered the woods, I planned to grab my hamstring, claiming a muscle pull. But jokes started right away, and I kept going to hear the punch lines. As I began to get really tired, they started telling gossip about the teachers. I didn't last long the first day, but pushed a bit farther with them day after day and started joining the political and psychological arguments.

Most of these cross country runners were on the academic honor roll. But the controversial arguments led me to believe that I was just as intelligent as the others. Each academic period my grades improved and I too, make the honor roll. More importantly, I had become a member of the group and set a new standard for myself due to group expectations.

I was most surprised about how good I felt after a run. The after-run attitude boost was better than I had experienced after any activity during my young life. The camaraderie and fun during those runs kept me coming back, and after 10 weeks I was hooked on endorphins and friendship. I continue to be . . . over 50 years later.

There is no doubt that running activated circuits inside me that started a search for my potential. I'm still on that journey. My greatest joy today is hearing the stories of those who have been able to enjoy life and overcome amazing challenges because they also discovered running.

Some of my very best runs were on days when I felt that I didn't have the energy to finish a mile. As my mind-body woke up, my spirit was transformed for the rest of the day.

Get out there and move the feet. There are some magical things that can happen.

© Polka Dot Images/Thinkstock

1   I run, therefore I am

Our mind-body organism is constantly adapting to make us better at what we do regularly. Running triggers a series of continual improvements because upgrades are needed in each of these areas: strong bones, efficient heart action, oxygen delivery, better and quicker thinking, and a higher level of awareness. While I enjoy these benefits, they are not why I am look forward to my run each day.

As you can read in the introduction, I was a fat, lazy, and unhappy 13-year-old when I started running. I was also struggling as a student. Within a few days of joining a group of distance runners, I felt better about myself, had more energy, and was better focused on my studies. Within a year, I was a good student, the weight was burning off and I was proud to have taken on the identity of a runner. When our family took a vacation, my first thought was "where can I run?"

As I became an adult, I began to make decisions based upon running. If I took that job, would my running time be reduced? Which of the affordable houses has the best running areas? If I married her, would she accept my running? Would she be a running partner as well as a marriage partner?

After I graduated from Wesleyan University, there was no running industry and no hope of making a living from the lifestyle activity that I loved. The only reason to run, as perceived by the general population and the runners I knew at the time, was to move to the next competitive level. But I sensed that there was something more powerful that pulled me out for my run each day. First, I felt better after a run than at any other time of the day.

As substantial as the physical/medical benefits from running are, the mental and emotional benefits are far greater. Running changes us, month after month, year after year. It triggers and integrates multiple circuits that improve us in ways that enhance our health, life, and state of mind. The overall message that running sends throughout the mind-body network is that "I am getting better," "I enjoy this," and "I feel better about life."

What we do regularly modifies our thinking and behavior patterns. Aggressive sports tend to adapt participants into aggressive responses. Running tends to mold a person into positive contemplation, searching for potential, expanding current consciousness about making things better.

While running expands or maintains our physical capabilities and stamina at any age, it also activates the frontal lobe — the executive brain. Studies show that running stimulates activity within this decision-making center, where strategies are developed and problems are solved. This uniquely human command center can take control over emotional responses coming from the ancient subconscious brain, sort out issues, find creative solutions, and dig down for intuitive strength when needed.

Running has become a symbol of freedom. Just a few steps into a run and you can be disconnected from phones, texting, computer screens, demanding or aggravating people, and non-productive activities. You are on your own, self-reliant, self-sufficient, and empowered. When the pace is not stressful, the time on the run allows for positive thoughts and adaptations to occur. Just knowing that you will be receiving that freedom soon can reduce the stress of the day and improve attitude.

Running changes us. Studies and personality profiles show that as beginners continue to run regularly without time goals, they become more positive. As I work with runners, over months and years they tend to become more "self-starting," think and talk more honestly, and move on to other positive changes in their lives. Running triggers a series of circuits inside to gear up, improve capacity, become more efficient, expand awareness, focus, while instilling a sense that stress can be erased or managed, and problems solved.

I have many roles, but find that I can fulfill each better because I run. Running activates the positive life forces that make me more alive, think better, feel better with greater physical and mental stamina. So when someone asks me what I do, my response is automatic: "I'm a runner".

Running is only one of the aspects of my life that I treasure. But because I run, I enjoy all of the other areas better.

I run, therefore I am . . . whatever else I want to be.

2   Running gives me hope

Countless times I have seemingly hit a dead end during school, with family issues, with business problems, not having enough time, etc. In cases of ultimate frustration, I almost always put on the running duds and put one foot in front of the other.

Within 10 minutes, I feel better. The rhythm of the feet bestows a sense of stability. The forward motion communicates a sense of positive action.

Endorphins, the positive attitude hormones, send messages that things may be OK and getting better. Blood flow increases, and the mind-body network works together and revs up.

I'm running comfortably, with no significant huffing and puffing. I usually think about the problems, just staying in the moment. This is my world. This is the sacred place that I go to find my strengths.

The frontal lobe action starts gently, sorting things out. The logical left brain focuses on one issue at a time. No solutions, just the feeling that things will work out.

Very seldom is the issue resolved during one run. After the endorphins start hitting the receptor sites all over the body, problems drift into the background.

They're just not that important with all of the positive things going on. Attitude improves, vitality surges. There are possibilities!

The stress of failure melts away. The left brain has sorted the problem into a series of issues that can be confronted. Things are going to work out.

Hope emerges. The right brain generates some creative possibilities. A few minutes later this intuitive component usually sends subtle feelings of strength. It's doing the incredible job of connecting us with internal resources.

With hope, we feel secure and positive. Things will move forward again. After the run, there are many possibilities. I'm looking forward to my next run.

3   To use the powers that I have

Running puts us in touch with the basic feelings that energize us. During a run, we activate the components that make us more alive. I feel more alive when I connect with these instincts.

Even on days when I am too busy, I know that running will help. Because a good run turns on the switches that can make me more mentally efficient, I find that running for half an hour allows me to do two hours of work in 40 to 60 minutes.

Most citizens go through their week and never tap into the variety of good hormones injected during a run. I don't take these for granted. I enjoy the mental and emotional boost from a run, even when the physical side doesn't feel the best.

Each day I overcome lethargy and get out and run; I am empowered. The mind is clearer; the body has more vitality. The spirit is ready for the day.

It doesn't matter how unmotivated we are, there is energy and motivation inside us that can be tapped. Sometimes we may need to be a good robot: one foot, then the other. As soon as we get moving, we use our muscles, our heart and lungs, our brain. We feel more alive.

Running activates the frontal lobe – the conscious brain. This is the component that can make decisions, activate positive hormones, and take control over the subconscious negative messages of the reflex brain.

Realizing my potential for the day is empowering. That doesn't mean running fast or setting a personal record. Energy and attitude are boosted by a run at any pace, even with lots of walk breaks. With better energy and a good attitude, we are not only motivated to run but we have the momentum to do the things in our lives that we want/need to do.

Choose to run and your mind, body, and spirit can wake up together.

© Comstock Images/Thinkstock

4 In 30 minutes, I will feel good!

I just returned from a half-hour run, and I feel great. But I didn't feel good before and almost didn't get out the door. I've had so many of these "attitude turnarounds" that I don't let my feelings keep me from the wonderful boost I know will come after a workout.

Over fifty years ago, I was forced to choose a sport after my 8th grade classes. I didn't like to run because it was not fun and usually hurt. I chose winter cross country because some of my lazy friends told me that one could jog out to the woods (200 yards) and hide. However, due to the bonding and joking of the cross country runners, I wanted to run each day. I was pleasantly surprised that even after a really tough run, I felt better than I used to feel at any other time.

Half a century later, the treasury of after-run rewards is as wonderful as it was on the first day. I've not found such a boost of attitude, vitality, or mental energy in any other activity. Thousands of runners have told me that they have had the same experience.

Sometimes I don't feel good during a single minute of the run. But I've learned that with a few adjustments and a refusal to quit, I'm rewarded. On certain days, you simply have to dig down and keep going. Each time you do this, I believe that the subconscious brain activates a "switch" that makes it easier to get through the next challenging workout with resources to help you through.

The first segment of a low-motivation run is usually the toughest, so go slowly (no huffing and puffing). The most common mistake is running too fast. This increases stress, which triggers negative attitude hormones.

But when the pace is easy enough, the body can relax, stress is released, and positive attitude secretions lock into receptors. The messages sent throughout your mind-body network are all good, confident, and positive.

Walk breaks help turn the mind around. They erase fatigue and stress when taken often enough. The run/walk/run strategy also allows you to receive endorphins, whose first job is to manage the pain produced when you run continuously.

But endorphins have a beneficial side effect: an attitude boost. These natural hormones are among the most powerful positive attitude peptides produced. Most people who run continuously only experience the effect after a run. During a walk, the endorphins lock into receptor sites, leaving you with a positive glow, walk break after walk break.

Running has also been shown to activate the frontal lobe – the conscious brain. This allows us to manage stress, and take control over our life and attitude. Inside this uniquely human brain component, you can set up a strategy for each part of each run, and for the rest of the day.

Sometimes it takes 15 minutes, sometimes 20 and occasionally 30 minutes, but you can feel amazingly good if you're not exceeding the speed limit.

Enjoy every endorphin!

Getting started on a tough day

- Pace must be slow enough
- Caffeine helps to get out the door
- When in doubt, walk more
- Start slowly – no huffing and puffing
- How to get out the door when unmotivated: see page 75
- How to keep going when you tend to slow down: see page 134, 136
- How the frontal lobe is activated to solve problems: see page 34

5 I'm a nicer person because I run

Most of us experience a few days a year when the stress level is such that we are not as humane as we should be toward others. Family members, co-workers, and friends often push runners out the door for a workout on such days because they know that there is usually an attitude change afterward.

A series of positive circuits are activated throughout the mind-body network when I run at a comfortable pace. This results in a better state of mind, which triggers improved confidence and energy. By the end of the run, I want to improve whatever I'm working on. I get more things done, have more energy to relate to my family, feel better, and work better. Without running, I wouldn't be the person I am.

Attitude adjustment: Studies show that as people get into running their personality profile improves in a positive direction. Over time, runners tend to have a more positive outlook and overall attitude. Even after one run, I feel better about myself and better about the future. Running every other day brings consistency to this attitude improvement. It has always amazed me how a run can change one's perspective.

I've always sensed that I think better after a run. Now there's research to prove it. Cognitive test results are better after 30 minutes on the treadmill. Running seems to unblock mental logjams and rev up mental energy. This helps me be a better parent, husband, project leader, coach, writer, problem solver, and friend.

Individual responsibility for health: Running makes me aware of my capabilities and physical limitations. Running has prepared me to expect to have a general feeling of well-being and to know that something is wrong when I don't. This allows for quick medical action if needed. I've only had two colds in the past 10 years. I believe that being conscious of maintaining long-term health triggers other circuits that make us more likely to respond to other warning signs.

More vitality: Just the thought that I will get an activity boost from my run energizes my day. I look forward to the workout, which reduces stress buildup. During the run, I feel really alive. Afterward, the energy circuits are turned on for hours, mentally and physically.

I feel better! Running helps to put my mind, body, and spirit into balance. This bestows a glow that I don't get from any other activity. Because I feel better, I think better. I want to help people, take care of my responsibilities, improve my communication and projects, and enjoy my family.

Be nice to your friends, family members, and yourself – get out and run

© Goodshoot/Thinkstock

6   RUNNING: A partial list of benefits

- These are a few of the benefits I've experienced during more than 50 years of running.
- Can enhance the cardiovascular system
- Can greatly improve fat burning capacity
- Stimulates new brain cell growth
- Activates the use of the frontal lobe (conscious brain)
- Speeds up circuits in frontal lobe that make decisions
- Can greatly reduce stress
- Significantly improves breathing capacity
- Triggers the release of positive attitude hormones
- Statistically increases lifespan by more than 2 hours for every hour spent running
- Improves overall vitality
- Significantly improves attitude
- Strengthens bones better than most sports
- Can allow joints to keep adapting as one gets older
- Bestows a unique sense of freedom
- Generates a sense of joy

7   I run for the sense of freedom

The only time I feel really free is during a run. Moving along under my own power while simply "being in the moment" allows me to appreciate the feeling of vitality without any expectation or judgment. I'm an emancipated animal expressing the life force of exertion.

What do I mean by "free?" It's a state of mind, an awareness level that is individually determined. Most important to me is the sensation that whatever I do during that run is OK. I then have the right to be in the moment. It took me several years to reach this state and about a decade more before I could lock into it whenever I wanted.

When I'm running, I don't have to think about anything, because I am the captain of my running ship and can steer it any way I want. I allow thoughts to hit me and go away. I'm open to feelings, which flow through me for a few minutes, are replaced by a quiet period and then another feeling. I enjoy the good thoughts and feelings but let the other ones pass on.

While pleasure and enjoyment can often be part of this mindset, they are not necessary. Reaching the "free zone" doesn't determine the success of a run. Regardless of the current demands of my life, when I reach this zone I am simply a part of the life force, expressing myself through forward movement.

Physical stress can kick you out of the zone. When the pace is just a bit too fast, or the walk breaks are not taken often enough, stress builds up. As soon as the overall stress level is perceived to be a bit too high, the subconscious reflex brain triggers a number of reactions that will interfere with the gentle environment needed for the "free zone": anxiety hormones, negative attitude hormones, and constriction of blood flow to key areas causing sensations of aches and pains. When I take command of my ship and slow down (often by walking more frequently), negative symptoms go away and are replaced by positive ones.

While running free, the mind-body network seems to communicate and calibrate components that are out of synch. Inside the frontal lobe, the left and right sides get balanced. The reflex brain and the frontal lobe adjust circuits. You feel under control and empowered.

When the right brain (creative and intuitive part of the human frontal lobe) is engaged, the runs are more likely to be in the "free zone." Others have described this as being on "cruise control." When tapping into the right side, I'm more likely to have creative thoughts, interesting images, and feel connected to intuitive sources of confidence and strength. Then I'm free to enjoy the rest of the run, moment by moment.

In this state, I imagine running along like my ancient ancestors. I'm part of the environment, interacting as an advance scout for the tribe. Feeling this connection brings me back to my roots.

I may be in the "free zone" for only a few moments, but those moments enrich my run and the rest of the day.

Exercise your freedom – run.

How I run in the "free zone"

- I stay away from phones, email and texting for at least 20 minutes before my run

- I carry no phone, no music

- I start out at a very conservative pace

- I take liberal walk breaks in the beginning: run 30 seconds/walk 30 seconds or 40 run/20 walk.

- No huffing and puffing

- I concentrate on gentle and smooth running

- If I feel any aggravation or sense of physical stress, I walk more

- I get into a comfortable rhythm of the feet

- I say my favorite mantras: "I feel good"; "I'm running free"; "I'm in the moment"

- During the walk breaks, I enjoy the sights around me

- During the run, I focus on how good it is to move forward

- I feel what I feel

- I think what I'm thinking

- I'm free for a while

- This moment is important

© PixLand/Thinkstock

8   Running: The best way to activate the spirit

I define the spirit as that part of us that wants to make things better and keeps us going when the rest of our mind-body is not working at current capacity. This is the source of inner strength that takes over when there doesn't seem to be resources to pull us through a tough experience.

Research has shown that when we believe that we can do something, internal circuits are turned on to make it happen. I believe that one of these interlocking resource networks is what I call the spirit.

Running has been the best way I've found to connect with my spirit. If I don't overload my system with stress during a run, there's almost always a positive attitude boost at the end. The regular pattern of running, with the resulting mental enhancement, activates one or more of the internal networks resulting in a lift when needed.

Regular activation of the circuits hardwires them into your subconscious reflex brain. So when a similar situation occurs, and you have prepared for that situation, the circuits are more likely to be activated. This is the spirit at work. It's no wonder that runners, in repeated personality profiles, show the highest level of positive attitude factors and the lowest on the depressive scale.

The spirit also finds resources to keep you going when there is little hope. Running at the right pace brings together body, mind and spirit. Some experts in ancient man I've interviewed believe that this was the edge that allowed our very primitive ancestors to survive before they developed the intelligence to make tools and coordinate hunting strategies. Two million years ago our relatives could not run as fast as the other animals and couldn't win a fight. The human spirit kept them going through major discomfort and fatigue. The more tenacious individuals survived to have children and have passed this capability to us.

The spirit boost that kept our Paleolithic relatives moving forward, when exhausted, with no energy in the tank, is imbedded in our DNA. It gets us out the door on the cold/hot days when we don't want to run, keeps us going when we want to quit, and pushes us to the finish when we aren't sure we can keep going.

You have the inner strength — get out and use it!

Engaging the spirit through running

- A 4-6 month training program simulates circuits to keep going the long distance treks made by our ancestors

- We program ourselves to improve

- We feel better after most runs

- This develops a more positive outlook on life

- During each challenge, the spirit pulls us on

- Progressively, we push longer through fatigue

- We learn that even under duress and doubt there are more resources

- Our spirit is ready to respond to challenges

Chapter 1:
The life-changing benefits of running

9   There's nothing better than a good run!

Even on the lowest motivation days, there's nothing like a run to make you feel really alive. Yes, it's sometimes hard to get off the bed or the couch. And yes, there's usually a warm-up period, during which you may not feel as good as you will later. But with the liberal use of walk breaks, and a gentle starting pace, you'll find the body "waking up" to the rhythm of the feet and the heart.

As you continue to move forward, the running muscles help to move blood throughout the body and mind. The nerves are firing and positive messages are being sent to billions of cells throughout the system within a few minutes. You start to wake up, then you feel better, and on the best days, you feel really alive.

No one has documented all of the positive things that happen inside of us when we run. We know that the heart pumps more blood to key areas, delivering the components for life enhancement. Increased heart action pulls the blood out of the exertion sites and returns it to the heart and lungs for an oxygen infusion.

Endorphins and other positive attitude hormones dramatically increase when we run. As they lock into the receptor sites, messages tell us intuitively that we

© Natalia Yakovlera/iStockphoto/Thinkstock

feel good, and things are getting better. Our whole body organism is smiling when we run at the right pace.

Running engages the conscious human brain, the frontal lobe. Problems are solved and intuitive connections are made to access resources.

When a run is paced correctly for you, on that day, there is an after-run glow that keeps on giving for the rest of the day.

Lace up those shoes, and get moving!

WHY RUN?

- Physical Rewards: Stronger heart, better oxygen transport, improved capillary network, lung function improvement, blood pressure maintenance, lowers cholesterol, and more.

- Endorphins: Triggers the release of the most powerful type of positive attitude hormones, locking into billions of receptor sites throughout the body.

- Vitality: When running at the right pace, energy level increases during the run and stays up for hours.

- Internal systems work together better: The intuitive circuits that manage energy, activity, repair and stress are programmed to come into balance when we exercise regularly.

- Aerobic running (no huffing and puffing) stimulates the energy circuit to come into better balance with the hunger circuit, allowing you the opportunity to reduce fat accumulation.

- Positive attitude adjustment: Even a short run can leave you feeling better about yourself and life than before the run. This can last for hours.

10 Running connects us with our endurance heritage

We were born to run and when we do so, many positive circuits are activated. There's a deep sense of satisfaction when we do something that takes us back to activities that helped ancient family members develop and find human identity. Running takes us way back – to the essence of our being.

Long before our ancestors learned to make and use tools, to hunt, or to farm, they had to keep moving all day long to acquire enough food to survive. Lacking the speed and strength of other animals, our inherently individualistic forebears survived, for at least a million years, because they covered long distances every day finding weeds, seeds, berries, etc., that were bypassed by other animals.

According to the experts, these day-long food gathering treks adapted the human body and mind for forward motion exertion while bestowing a sense of satisfaction and empowerment that is genetically embedded in each of us. When we get into a comfortable running rhythm, we can find, somewhere deep inside, pockets of emotional satisfaction. When we connect with patterns of success our mind-body rewards us. We are doing what we should do.

Various anthropologists have also tied the development of "human" traits to these endurance treks. One can assume that those who happened to be in groups had a higher survival rate. As they learned to communicate, share food gathering information, and protect one another, something magical happened: trust, cooperation, teamwork.

When we run/walk gently, we revisit positive feelings that our relatives have felt for millions of years. We are re-connecting with our roots in a very positive way. Run and enjoy the connection!

Gentle exertion – like our Paleolithic ancestors

- Start gently
- No huffing and puffing
- Have a more liberal amount of walking during the first 15 minutes
- Get into the rhythm of your feet, legs, and breathing
- Use a Galloway Timer – you don't have to look at your watch (www.jeffgalloway.com)
- Commit to a run-walk-run strategy that works for you

11 Running helps me think more clearly

Now there's research showing that regular aerobic endurance activity stimulates new brain cell growth at any age. Other research shows that after a 30-minute treadmill workout, subjects think better and quicker. What is happening inside the brain when we run?

As I did the research for my book *Mental Training*, I learned about the functions of the two major brain components: the ancient "reflex" brain and the "human brain" in the frontal lobe. The subconscious "reflex" brain conducts most of the life-sustaining activities, such as breathing, heart function, etc. This component has hundreds of stimulus-response behavior patterns that have been pre-programmed based upon our past experiences.

© Stockbyte/Thinkstock

The frontal lobe allows us to take conscious control over a situation and take action. It can override the subconscious brain. Strategies are developed and conscious actions are initiated in the frontal lobe that supersede the subconscious programming of the reflex brain. Other species do not have conscious frontal lobe capacity.

When we run, the frontal lobe is activated, giving us the capability of being "in the moment." We're solving problems, thinking ahead and taking control over our thoughts and actions. Runners tell me regularly that after hours of wrestling with a mental decision at work or home, it was during a run that the right solution became apparent.

So if you want to think better, get those shoes on and get out the door. Your mind and body will thank you.

© Comstock Images/Thinkstock

12 Running helps me control my emotions

Everyone has stress. A good run may not erase it, but it can reduce the effect and allow runners to gain control. This bestows a "mental fresh start" after the run to get on with what we need to do. Running is a proven attitude booster, and we need this when the emotions erupt.

Throughout the day, our stress level rises and falls like the stock market based upon issues at work, with family, with friends, etc. The subconscious "reflex" brain monitors stress levels because it is receiving communications constantly from all over the body and mind. When the overall stress increases to what the reflex brain believes to be a high level, anxiety hormones are released. If we continue to add to the pressure, negative attitude hormones are secreted.

All of this happens subconsciously. If we don't take conscious action to manage the stress, it's common to go into an emotional rollercoaster ride based upon which hormones are being produced at the moment.

Running activates the conscious brain, allowing you to reduce the production of negative attitude hormones and increase the secretion of positive ones. The focused action of this executive brain can override the reflex brain and give you control over your thoughts. Positive thoughts, can lead to the production of positive hormones.

Then, with a strategy of mental training, you can program the reflex brain to respond positively to challenges by taking a series of steps to get you through each problem. Each conscious, affirmative action can lower stress because you are taking control, activating positive thoughts and positive hormones.

But all of this starts with a few running steps that act like a switch to turn on the conscious brain and start the flow of positive emotions.

Step by step, you will become more positive. Get out there!

Emotional days . . . don't feel like running?

1.   Put on comfortable running clothes and shoes.

2.   Tell yourself that you are taking control.

3.   Walk out the door.

4.   Find a good mantra and say it, such as: "I'm moving forward," "I feel better," "I'm in control."

5.   Insert a 10-second run, followed by a 30 to 50-second walk.

6.   After several cycles of 10-second jogs, increase to 15 to 20 seconds/30-40 seconds of walking.

7.   Keep saying the mantra.

8.   Choose a strategy of running and walking that feels good but does not cause you to huff and puff.

9.   As you finish, choose a mantra that will set you up for the day: "I'm in control," "I feel good," "I am focused," "This is a good day."

10. Smile!

13 Running helps me manage pain

Many pains that we experience from injured body parts, may be induced or aggravated by stress. Running at the right pace can turn down the stress volume and turn on the blood flow. In many cases, increased blood flow can significantly reduce or eliminate the pain within a few minutes.

© NinaMalyna/iStockphoto/Thinkstock

The "reflex" brain (our ancient and subconscious center), when suffering a stress overload, will reduce blood flow to areas it knows to be damaged. This condition is called tension myositis syndrome, or TMS. When investigated by experts, such as orthopedist John Sarno, (Mindbody Prescription) the amount of damage does not justify the amount of pain. Subconscious blood constriction by the reflex brain can result in debilitating pain or nagging, chronic pain.

As noted in my book Mental Training, Dr. Sarno and others have found that one does not need to eliminate stress to get relief from pain or negative attitude hormones. By shifting control to the frontal lobe, runners can manage the situation by first acknowledging that stress is the cause, and then using a cognitive strategy to stay in the conscious brain.

As successful strategies are developed, the reflex brain can be retrained to avoid an overload. Running tends to activate the conscious brain. When the first hint of TMS is felt, use the cognitive strategy in the attached TMS section and talk back to the reflex brain.

Making these simple conscious statements can turn the control switch to the frontal lobe. Then you can visualize the capillaries in the weak link opening up as you say, "That's it, open up the flow, more blood is flowing, pain is going away." These statements, with the conscious mental focus, can keep the reflex brain from shutting off blood flow due to stress. Have fun with this.

Managing pain

Dr. John Sarno is an orthopedist who practiced traditional medicine for years. He discovered a condition called TMS, along with methods of treating it. This dramatically improved his cure rate. I recommend his books, *Mindbody Prescription* and *Healing Back Pain*, because they have helped thousands of people manage or eliminate chronic pain, and get on with their lives.

As the runner starts a workout, it helps to identify sources of stress and "talk them out" or just vent as you're moving down the road. Dr. Sarno says that you don't have to resolve an issue to mange or cure the pain – you just need to be aware of it, and then take some conscious action to move control away from the reflex brain.

Sarno explains how inner stress buildup activates TMS. The reflex brain receives the continuous information flow through the peptide network, which identifies the areas of the body that have been damaged.

Each of us has certain "weak links" that tend to hurt more often than other areas. When total stress levels rise significantly for the individual, the reflex brain reduces blood flow to these areas, dramatically increasing pain. But when patients take conscious control over the reflex brain by deciding to do things like make conscious statements, the blood flow can be restored and there can be a re-programming of the reflex brain.

"I know what you are doing, reflex brain, and I won't allow it."

"Open up the flow in my _____"

"I'm in control here."

"I'm not going to let the reflex brain control the blood flow."

Note: Not all aches and pains are due to TMS. Before running, when there is pain, get guidance from your doctor to ensure that some running/walking will not make the condition worse. It's best to be under the care of a doctor who understands TMS and wants you to run if you can.

Note: For more information on the causes behind TMS and how they apply to running, see *Mental Training*.

14 Running motivates me for the rest of the day

I always receive mental momentum after my run that continues for the rest of the day. The muscles come alive, injecting physical energy into my movements. Mental energy increases as the executive brain gets organized and adjusted to a higher level of activity. Because running stimulates positive attitude hormones, the subconscious reflex brain senses that things are as they should be and sends good attitude hormones throughout the system delivering a glow of good feelings and confidence.

When we run gently, with appropriate walk breaks, we're using the muscles the way they were designed to be used. We're in harmony with the natural function of the body and things are in balance. A state of harmony stimulates the reflex brain to continue to boost mental attitude.

Confession: At the start of a run, I often don't feel "on track" for the day. I often sense that several key activities for the day are "tasks." After a few minutes, I find myself stimulated by the trees, the trail, the wind. The stress of everyday life goes away as I appreciate the sensation of moving forward, touching the ground, feeling the gentle beat of the life sustaining heart, and enjoying the air coming and going from mouth to lungs.

Then the endorphins kick in. These positive attitude hormones are among the most powerful and can have a "hangover effect" in a good way.

Even a short run produces an empowerment that keeps pinging me all day long. I'm ready for my day. Gone is the term "task." Each project is an opportunity.

Achievement: Moving ourselves on foot gives one a genuine sense of accomplishment. When your feet and muscles "conquer" several miles, you receive an authentic satisfaction based upon real work. This is one of the simple but satisfying rewards that have been passed on by our primitive ancestors. Bottom line is that we feel better about ourselves when we have covered some distance on that day. There is even more enhanced self-esteem in pushing back your current endurance level. As you keep going farther on long runs, you feel an inner glow not experienced in other activities.

Empowerment
- You are pulling from resources that are inside you
- You find yourself becoming more intuitive as the right brain kicks in
- You feel the confidence to grapple with a problem that is not solvable
- You find that you have more internal strength and creativity than you thought
- This enhanced feeling of energy and empowerment carries into other areas of life

15 Run and receive a vitality boost

Runners tell me that they feel better after a run than after any activity. When injured, athletes just don't feel like themselves. Many alternative activities have been tried. I've never heard a runner say that another activity bestowed as good a boost as running.

Even when you run in short segments (such as running 10 seconds every minute), the demands of the running motion force the body to gear up. The central nervous system turns on a lot of switches, activating the heart, lungs, muscles, energy production. Systems of balance must be enhanced. The necessary focus on the surface ahead and the awareness of safety and health issues increase awareness of surroundings.

All of these upgrades result in an overall boost in activity throughout the mind-body network. The reflex brain subconsciously turns on a lot of switches and integrates the many components into a team.

If the pace is correct, the gentle, enhanced workload bestows a sustainable increase in activity throughout the organism. You feel energized to do the next thing on your list.

The vitality boost keeps on giving as you feel more alive after a run. All of the systems are running well and you are ready for the rest of your day.

Lingering benefits of vitality increase

More productivity, less fatigue. Those who insert a gentle workout into the day tend to be more productive and less tired than those who don't.

Pushing back your physical capacity for life. I regularly see runners in their 70s and 80s who don't look their age. When I look closely, the face and skin may give a general indication, but the vitality, mental energy, and good attitude would indicate a person who is one or two decades younger than predicted.

Mental energy. Even when the body is tired, a good run can turn on better activity in the frontal lobe. This is the area that organizes, solves problems, and designs strategy.

© PBananaStock/Thinkstock

16 Running brings together body, mind, and spirit better than any activity I know

The overall experience you receive from the forward momentum of running is more positive that the sum of the individual benefits. The blending of enhancements in body, mind, and spirit give one an empowerment that is unique.

Muscles and body parts are designed to be exercised and thrive when they move in normal ways. After a well-paced run, you can just feel the muscle cells smiling. If you're not feeling this way, insert more walk breaks.

© Eric Hood/iStockphoto/Thinkstock

Your subconscious (reflex) brain monitors activity throughout the body and keeps you going. It has a multitude of stimulus-response behavior patterns that are activated when you run. This amazing brain component manages and adjusts blood flow to the muscles, increases heart rate, monitors heat buildup, etc. This "reflex" brain monitors, subconsciously, overall stress and takes action when an overload situation is perceived.

The frontal lobe of your brain is engaged in a major way when you run. The left side (logical, math, etc.) solves problems and conducts cognitive strategies to maintain focus while the right side (creative and intuitive) entertains and can connect to inner strengths when needed.

I define "spirit" as the series of internal circuits that keep us going under stress, fatigue, low motivation, and adversity. Running turns on the switches to the circuits of the spirit, leaving one with a sense of well-being and worth that can help deal with challenges in running and other areas of life.

The bodies we inherited have responded to running challenges for millions of years. The blending of our body, mind, and spirit has been so finely tuned that it happens seamlessly when we run.

You just have to take the first step . . . then the second.

17 Running gets me "in the moment"

A relaxing run can give you perspective on your day, your priorities, and your life. Running will shift you into your conscious brain. This frontal lobe area is the "human brain" that makes decisions, sets up strategies, and gives you control over your run, your motivation, and your day.

Look around you during the walk breaks. Enjoy the plants, trees, flowers. Salute the animals. Dogs, rabbits, and squirrels are marvelous creatures with interesting behavior patterns.

If running through a neighborhood, notice the architecture of the houses. See how they are constructed. Are they landscaped? On which street would you like to live? Alter a habitual course by at least a block to see "new territory."

How is your body responding to the weather? Is the wind getting stronger? How do you like the temperature? If it's hot, slow down and take more frequent walk breaks. If it's cold, run into the wind during the first half of the run.

If you don't feel right at current pace, adjust it. If you feel good, run a bit faster for a few steps to rev up your vitality and mental attitude.

For more transcendental moments, settle into a comfortable rhythm of running and walking and let the right brain entertain or sort things out. This is the subconscious part of the frontal lobe that activates creativity and intuitive strength.

You are feeling the life within you – body, mind, and spirit. You are in control and can adjust as needed.

This is when the fun begins!

To get into the moment:

- Gentle warm up: No huffing and puffing

- Course: Familiar so that you can go into "cruise control" and not get lost

- No expectations for the run in time or distance

- Notice something every minute or two

- If you're feeling bored, change the speed or the course slightly

- Even if you feel great at the end, don't sprint

18 Running triggers my creativity and intuitive strength

By staying within your capabilities and getting into the rhythm of the run, it's possible to activate your right brain, and tap into the subconscious side of your frontal lobe. Many runners describe their right brain runs as "transcendental."

The right side frontal lobe is the center of creativity and intuition. This component can connect you to hidden strengths to keep you going when challenged. It can make adaptations for better efficiency and smoother running.

The right brain has memory. After you've worked through a problem in the past, it can steer you through a similar set of solutions when the problem appears again. In many cases, you have no idea how the right brain did this, you simply realize that the problem has been taken care of.

When you're in the right brain, you'll generally feel more calm and under control. Creative, sometimes crazy, thoughts will occur. Interesting ideas will pop up.

Stimulate right brain activity by reading an interesting problem, quote, or idea before you start. Some runners find that certain types of music can be a catalyst.

If you want to stay under right brain control, don't huff and puff. Exertion stress will kick you out of this restorative center.

Shift to the right side and cruise.

Running with the right brain

1. Start slowly and stay at a comfortable pace.

2. Run in a park, rail trail, or other area where there's no cross street traffic.

3. During each walk break, look around and enjoy the scenery.

4. Find a mantra that you can say to the rhythm of your feet.

5. Have several mantras that are creative and non logical that stimulate interesting thoughts.

6. No huffing and puffing.

19 Running formats my brain

At the beginning of a morning run, even after a strong cup of coffee, it often takes my brain several minutes to figure out how I'm going to do all the things that I need to do that day. But I know from experience that within thirty minutes, as I get into the rhythm of my run, at least the first half of my day will be organized.

Running switches on circuits in the frontal lobe. This conscious brain can analyze your current situation and challenges, set priorities, design strategies and much more. Even on the mental fog days, I will say to myself, over and over, "set up the day," or "what do we need to do first."

The first series of messages are in the category that I call "mental garbage." These unresolved issues are recognized, sorted, and prioritized. Most are pushed aside within a few minutes, and then I'm ready for the next set.

The frontal lobe churns and sorts. Issues are brought up and recognized. Concerns are addressed. Priorities are assigned. Plans are initiated. All of this is happening while I'm enjoying the endorphins, and experiencing the air, sunlight, flora, and fauna.

As the conscious brain works, positive attitude hormones are produced. I feel better about the day. Ideas pop up from both logical and creative sides and are sorted out.

By the end of the run, my day has structure, and I feel good. I feel confident that even the unknowns can be put into a format and handled.

I'm ready!

Formatting of the brain

- As you prepare for the morning run (while drinking coffee, etc.), visualize how the run is going to make you feel good.

- Smile

- Make an affirmative statement, such as "Running makes me feel good"

- Tell your brain to start the formatting

- "I feel things are sorting out"

20 Running brings out guttural/intuitive strengths and fun

I feel more alive and "in the moment" when I run. Thousands of others have told me that they were very surprised to discover this aspect of running, but this is what keeps them coming back, run after run.

One of my first guttural fun runs was during an unexpected hard rainstorm. I was several miles from my home as my clothes got soaked and my shoes filled up with water. At first, I was mad. In my frustration, I picked up the pace in order to jump over a puddle in the road. As I landed, I had to laugh at my instincts: My shoes couldn't get any more wet and yet I was avoiding a small puddle in the road. During the rest of the run I felt like a little kid splashing through the puddles or jumping over them.

When runners talk on a run, they often connect much more quickly on common issues or past experiences than when having coffee together. There is an intuitive connection that was developed a million years ago. Primitive ancestors had to quickly evaluate whether they could trust a travel companion, what each should be responsible for, and whether there was a serious problem that required care. There is also a respect that flows from one runner to another for covering the distance.

The survival of the tribe often depended upon each person doing his share of the exertion, while working together and backing one another up. Without these behaviors, food gathering and protection from predators would be compromised.

In most areas of modern life, these intuitive responses aren't needed. Primitive Paleolithic instincts come out during a run as we tend to react honestly to those with whom we are running. Secrets are shared, along with confessions. What is said on a run, stays on a run. It is amazing how intuitively this unspoken agreement is assumed.

Guttural fun is another primitive joy. Runners tend to feel more confident doing or saying something silly during a run when compared to other experiences in life. Often within one run, group members will play gentle tricks or jokes on one another.

When groups are running together at a comfortable pace, you'll tend to hear a lot of laughing.

21 Running gets the body into a high level of readiness

- Heart and lung function must increase significantly

- Feet must be ready to adapt to any terrain

- Vision must process surface issues, the path ahead

- The balance area of the brain must adapt to a more challenging environment

- The energy system must supply muscles, sugar for the brain

- Dozens of other functional circuits get revved up

Your mind-body organism goes on high alert and is geared up for greater capacity when you start running. This bestows a higher level of vitality and mental focus.

It would be mentally tiring if you had to consciously think through each of these operations to get them going and keep them going, but you don't. When you decide to run, the frontal lobe tells the reflex brain to gear up. Subconsciously, it activates the circuits that will be needed, and then fine-tunes them for the intensity of exertion.

When the pace is within your capabilities and you have strategic walk breaks, the system is coordinated, like a team of workers who love their job and love working together with the other team members. There is harmony.

Running stimulates the body to increase activity, while frequent walk breaks keep you from debilitating fatigue, overuse or depletion of resources. So you receive an increase in vitality without the breakdown of weak links or an increase in stress level stimulating negative hormones.

This intuitive balance is fine-tuned throughout a run as long as pace and walk breaks are within current capabilities. The frontal lobe anticipates new challenges and signals the reflex brain to get it done.

The best part to me is that this mind-body readiness keeps me revved up for the rest of the day.

© Robert Reere/iStockphoto/Thinkstock

22 Running helps me solve problems

When I can't find a solution to a current issue, I go out on a run. The pace must be slow. Too much exertion for that day will increase stress and interfere with many of my problem-solving patterns.

On problem-solving runs, I start so slowly that there is no huffing and puffing. I'm enjoying moving forward, feeling the exertion of the legs, muscles, heart and lungs. Then my left brain (logic) goes through various aspects of the problem. That's the signal that I'm in the frontal lobe. The conscious brain breaks down the problem into manageable pieces. Sometimes I will instantly see new aspects of the problem.

On other days, the activity shifts to the right side because logic can only go so far in solving difficult problems. I'll re-focus for a while on what's going on around me: the trees, clouds, people, and other animals. I'm an animal during those moments, and I enjoy being one.

The walk break helps me make the shift into the right side of the frontal lobe. This center of creativity has innovation and intuition, which can unlock many seemingly dead-end problems. It subconsciously makes connections and comes up with creative solutions time after time.

Again, the pace must be slow for the right side to work its magic. Faster running builds up stress, which tends to shut off the free-flowing action of the right brain.

So the left side sets up the issues and breaks them into manageable pieces. It also identifies the key problems. This allows the right brain to work on creative solutions or find inner resources to "face up to it," "dig down deeper," or try a different approach.

The problem may not be solved by the end of the run, but the process has started. I almost always come away from a run feeling that a solution can be found. Without the work done on the run, I am sure that many of my problems would not have been taken care of.

I'm ready to tackle another challenge. I'm ready to run!

Setting up a problem-solving run

- Run slowly – the frontal lobe is activated by running, but too much stress reduces effectiveness

- Get into a rhythm – provides structure, stimulation, and positive environment for both left and right brain activity

- Have a mantra – it should mention the problem, or be a positive statement, "I can solve this"

- Laugh and smile – this opens up the positive hormones and stimulates right brain activity

- Think of the problems and say "I can do it" 3-5 times, regularly

- Enjoy every minute of your run

23 Running gets me into the right rhythm – for the day

Some days seem to flow, but others just rattle through a series of interruptions. Most of the runners I've talked to about this topic have disclosed that they have a certain sense of rhythm during a run that feels comfortable, especially at the start. A morning run can help us find a good rhythm for the day.

Feet have nerve connections that extend throughout the body. As you move yourself forward, messages go out from the feet, to gear up the various components that you'll need on your run, and for the activities of the day.

When we push our workouts or our schedule of appointments too fast, the systems get overloaded. Running – especially early in the morning – teaches us to warm up gently and allow time for the key components to work as a team. A gentle but steady rhythm can help in many ways.

Wake up the feet and you wake up the mind. Experts believe that the sense of rhythm experienced by our ancient ancestors in their continual migrations on foot hardwired our brains for patterns that later became chants, cadence songs,

© vndrpttn/iStockphoto/Thinkstock

music, dance, etc. One foot after another, establishing a comfortable rhythm, formats the timing part of the brain.

As you start the run, don't worry about the pace. Try to find a gentle foot pattern. Stay smooth. Enjoy the natural motion of your feet and legs keeping you in touch with the earth.

Taking walk breaks doesn't have to interrupt your rhythm. Galloway timers are now available that beep or vibrate so that you don't have to monitor this. These devices seem to format the reflex brain into a run/walk/run rhythm.

Let the feet find their rhythm. Use a mantra, song, cadence that feels natural to you. Once your right brain is monitoring rhythm, it makes adjustments subconsciously.

Some use a mantra, song, or cadence statement (as used in boot camp). As long as this is a natural pattern for you on that day, this can be motivating. I don't like the idea of trying to increase cadence by using a metronome because this forces you to use an instrument instead of develop the intuitive timing within yourself.

Run to your own beat.

24 "I've done something" when I finish my run

For over 50 years, almost every run has delivered an intuitive sense of accomplishment. Nothing else in my life has delivered such a consistent feeling of worth.

During the first few months of running, I felt better after a run (even a tough one) than I used to feel at any time. After a tough academic or social day, I did not look forward to my run. But mile after mile, my spirits would be lifted.

Work frustration is common. During my term in the Navy, for example, my run helped me deal with various military and people issues. As I explored new seaport running routes and connected with runners from other cultures, I erased stress and expanded my awareness.

As I have dealt with the stress and challenges of being a small business owner for over 40 years, running has helped me stay focused. Whatever the problems, I knew that my run would give me a positive state of mind. Even when there didn't seem to be a good solution to a business problem, a good run bestows a sense that I will get through it. Most of my solutions have come during or immediately after a run.

There's something wonderfully do-able about being able to move your feet for 30 minutes or more around the neighborhood. On frustrating days, that one accomplishment can break the cycle of stalemate and start a chain of positives. As I do this day after day, mind/body anticipates the many rewards, and I feel better before the run, knowing that I will run later.

Running accomplishment comes from the boost to the spirit. We look at life differently when the spirit is up. Major concepts become engaging, petty bickering moves into the background, and the focus tends to be on possibilities rather than problems.

You are then free to enjoy the run and the satisfaction and accomplishment that lingers.

You are in control.

25 Enjoy a lasting sense of accomplishment

It's going the distance – not the finish times or age group placement – that matters.

The human organism is a complex network of circuits that generates emotions and sensations after we do, say, or think about something. Exercise can trigger positive hormones and stimulate the executive part of the brain to give us control.

The finishing of a long race brings inner satisfaction that often lasts for months or years. This is probably due to the connections with circuits that rewarded our ancient ancestors for continuing to cover distance on foot until they found adequate food or got away from predators.

But focusing on time improvement or age group place activates the ego circuits. There is often some satisfaction when we run fast in a race or workout, but this is short-lived. The ego is constantly projecting us forward to new improvements that are often not within the current range of possibility. At some point, this produces frustration and disappointment due to the stress buildup, which triggers negative attitude hormones.

Faster ego time projections often lead to faster workouts, which lead to aches, pains, and burnout. But by setting up realistic goals and strategically managing the workouts and the race, this can be a meaningful challenge, especially when running with a partner or team.

Races can motivate us. An event on the appointment calendar can inspire us to train well, focus on getting in all of the workouts, and activate the frontal lobe to set up a strategy. When time goals are a small piece of the goal focus, they can provide interesting stimulation.

But when the major source of satisfaction is in the finish time, the number of negatives often exceed the positives. The actual finish time is based upon a lot of factors that are beyond one's control: weather, crowd, metabolic issues.

Exclusive focus on time goals often results in a loss of what I believe are the true treasures of running: inner freedom, enjoyment of the act of running in the moment, and satisfaction in crossing the finish line.

Finishing is winning. Cross the finish line of your choice!

26 Running improves my attitude

Studies over the decades have shown that runners have some of the highest positive attitude levels and the lowest scores on the negative mood scale. Other studies report that positive attitude factors increase as a runner continues to run.

When I started running I was a fat, lazy 13-year-old who wasn't happy. My attitude worsened during the early weeks of my 8th grade year when I was forced to enroll in after-school physical fitness activities (football was my choice for fall). During the winter, I chose winter cross country because of the lenient coach. I was amazed at how good I felt, even after the toughest run.

© Eric Hood/iStockphoto/Thinkstock

Hormones influence attitude. Specific types of hormones are produced based upon what we are experiencing, our level of stress, what we believe, and what we are doing. These substances lock into receptor sites on billions of cells throughout the body and send messages back to the brain.

Physical or psychological stress will trigger negative hormones, which are subconsciously monitored by the reflex brain. The higher the stress, the more negative the hormones, leading to low motivation, negative attitude, and ultimately to depression.

Running offers two ways to avoid this negative mental downturn. A comfortable running pace stimulates endorphins – some of the most powerful positive attitude hormones. These lock into receptor sites making us feel better and then pretty darn good (if the pace is under control).

Running also activates the human brain, the frontal lobe. This mental component can override the production of negative hormones by the subconscious brain as one takes control over the situation.

OK, get out the door and crank out those endorphins!

27 Jumpstart your motivation

Almost every runner feels better after almost every run. But there are "those" days every year when the subconscious reflex brain is under a higher level of stress/pressure. The higher the stress, the more negative attitude hormones produced, spreading low motivation messages throughout the mind-body system.

By taking conscious action, you can override the reflex brain, feel better and get moving. Each of the simple actions below can improve mental attitude to get out the door and keep going when you are challenged. Each action can also stimulate the secretion of the positive attitude hormones that make you feel better physically and emotionally. As you take one step after another, you will gradually increase the flow of the "good attitude" substances and gain control over your motivation.

- Eat a blood sugar boosting snack if needed – Low blood sugar is a major stress on the brain. A simple snack of about 100 calories can often change one's attitude in 20-30 minutes. Some runners have had a rebound by taking a sip or two of a sugar beverage and spitting it out.

- Drink a cup of coffee – If you like coffee and have no problems consuming it, try a cup. Caffeine is a central nervous system stimulant and helps with focus. Even one cup of coffee has been shown to increase endurance on treadmill tests.

- Start Walking – The gentle motion of walking will stimulate secretions of peptides, improving mood and motivation.

- Smile – Smiles not only activate endorphins. A smile tends to bestow confidence and a feeling of control over the situation.

- Breathe in cadence with your steps – Rhythmical breathing has been shown to reduce stress and improve attitude. Take a lower lung breath every 3rd or 4th breath.

- Believe that you will feel better, and that you are doing something positive for yourself. Of course you are doing this. Your positive belief in what you are doing activates positive peptides.

- Lower the intensity of the workout/race – If you are feeling stress/pressure when considering a pace of 9 min/mi., run 10 min/mi. If a 3-1 ratio seems too challenging, try a 1-1. Running shorter segments often leaves you feeling so strong that you increase speed at the end or at least "feel strong" afterward.

Chapter 2
I want to overcome my challenges

28 No more exhaustion

Many runners or former runners build barriers (of potential fatigue/discomfort) that keep them from running. The most common mistaken concept that I am proud to denounce is that you must run continuously to get the advantages of running.

Any amount of running and walking will improve your health and spirit. When you break down the self-imposed barriers by running a short time segment followed by a walk break, you can avoid severe fatigue while receiving the endorphin effect. When you run, endorphins are produced to deal with muscle pain. During a walk break, without pain to deal with, the endorphins lock into receptor sites throughout the body, sending the positive message that you feel good – because you do.

Once running, you can find the best ratio of running and walking for you on that day. You're in control, increasing the run portion when you feel good, increasing

the walk segment on the tough days. If you start more gently, you will often finish strong. Exercising control improves motivation. Being in control over your destiny is personally empowering.

Just walking will get me going. On the super-low motivation days, walk. Once I get out there, the body and mind get into a better state, and I can insert small amounts of running. As the endorphins kick in, the run segments can be adjusted. For example: If you don't feel up to running with your usual strategy of (run three minutes/walk one minute), start with 1-1 or 30 seconds/30 seconds or 15 seconds running/45 seconds walking.

Knowing that one can cover just about any distance is also empowering. With the right combination of run-walk-run, you can continue to erase fatigue and push your endurance wall back, walk break by walk break.

I walk strategically and run farther!

29 I'm in control

Thousands of runners tell me every year that they started running only because they discovered my run-walk-run method. Until then, most thought that you had to run continuously in order to "run," and they originally tried to do this. When they became winded, exhausted, sore, or nauseous, they assumed that their bodies weren't designed for running.

Everything changed when they started inserting walk breaks after a few minutes (or a few seconds) into the run: huffing and puffing stopped, pain went away, and muscles were strong to the finish. Replacing the negatives was the glow of accomplishment along with a better attitude and vitality that enhanced their run and their life. YOU CAN, TOO!

© Brand X/Thinkstock

I doubt that you will find any training component that will help you in more ways than my run-walk-run method. I continue to be amazed, every week, at the reports of how strategic walk breaks help runners enjoy every run, even those that started out as difficult. When placed appropriately for the individual, walk breaks will erase debilitating tiredness, reduce stress, improve motivation, increase running enjoyment, speed recovery, and allow the runner to finish with strength.

When you focus on a strategy of run/walk/run or change it, you shift mental action into your frontal lobe, the strategy center. This allows you to control pace and your comfort zone. Conscious activity in the frontal lobe overrides the subconscious reflex brain where stress can trigger negative emotions.

You can gain control now by walking early and often. This allows you to be strong to the end and recover fast. By having a strategy, monitoring your breathing, and making adjustments, you can stay mentally focused. There is no need to be totally exhausted at the end of any long run.

Walk breaks...

- Give you control over the entire training process

- Erase fatigue

- Push back your fatigue wall

- Allow for endorphins to collect during each walk break – you feel good!

- Break up the distance into manageable units ("two more minutes")

- Speed recovery

- Reduce the chance of aches, pains, and injury

- Allow you to feel good afterward and to carry on the rest of your day without debilitating fatigue

- Give you all of the endurance from the distance covered in each session – without the pain

- Allow older or heavier runners to recover faster and feel as good or better as their younger (slimmer) days

For more information on walk breaks, see www.jeffgalloway.com where you can find a timer that beeps and/or vibrates for the amount of running and walking you wish.

30 I don't have to run a marathon . . . only one minute at a time

The goal of finishing a long race is quite motivating. The crossing of the finish line after a meaningful training journey is amazingly empowering. And you never have to break down or hit an endurance wall.

You can melt the fatigue and stress of any distance now by running a short segment and then walking to erase the running fatigue. If you perceive a run is stressful when you are running 5 minutes/walking 1 minute, then use a 3-1 or 1-1 or 20-second run/40-second walk.

Running continuously during a segment that is too long for you, on that day, will result in extreme fatigue, slowdown, and physical exhaustion. There is no ratio that is set in stone. You are empowered to take control over your fatigue in advance by adjusting the walk breaks.

The human psyche wants to be in control. Probably the best benefit of run-walk-run is that you are in command over how you feel during and after a run. So you can enjoy the endorphins that are produced by the run while avoiding the negatives. Each time you walk, you exercise your power during that moment.

Walk breaks dissolve two types of stress: physical and psychological. Stress to the muscles, tendons, joints, and nerves can be managed with the appropriate run-walk-run strategy for the day. Lowering your physical stress will lower your psychological stress. This means that you can reduce the negative attitude hormones and allow the positive endorphins to lock into receptors and send messages of well-being.

Finding the right strategy for the next few moments is all you have to do. You have the power to do this and therefore control how good you can feel throughout your run. Then you will enjoy the attitude adjustment afterward that can last for the rest of the day.

Run-walk-run strategies

- The most important walk breaks are the first ones
- The longer the run segment, the more fatigue
- Most of the benefit from a walk break occurs during the first 30 seconds of walking
- In races, it is fine to reduce walk break use during the last 15-30%
- Don't use a long stride – keep the hamstrings from getting extended

PACE/MI   RUN/WALK

(It's always appropriate to adjust to a more gentle strategy)

6:00 min/mi – run a mile/walk 20 seconds
7:00 min/mi – run a mile/walk 30-40 seconds
7:30 min/mi – run 5 min/walk 30-40 seconds
8:00 min/mi – run 4 min/walk 30 seconds
8:30 min/mi – run 4 min/walk 45 seconds
9:00 min/mi – run 4 min/walk 1 min (4-1)
10:00 min/mi – 3-1
11:00 min/mi – 2-1 or 2.5-1
12:00 min/mi – 2-1
13:00 min/mi – 1-1
14:00 min/mi – 30-sec-30-sec
15:00 min/mi – 20-sec run/40-sec walk
16:00 min/mi – 15-sec run/45-sec walk
17:00 min/mi – 10-sec run/50-sec walk

© Comstock Images/Thinkstock

31 Running can change a negative mindset into a positive one

What you think, say, and believe can stimulate the release of either positive or negative hormones. When we are bothered by a stressful situation or recent setback and we dwell on it, stress builds up in the subconscious brain, which releases negative hormones. If we continue to focus on the negative and we believe that a situation will turn out badly for us, more stress will accumulate. At first we feel anxious, but an increase in negative peptides triggers waves of negative emotions.

Stress is a fact of life. We can choose to deal with it or let the subconscious reflex brain control our emotions. Focusing on how stressful things are, or how bad we feel, will allow the reflex brain to pump out negative hormones. Not only does this leave us feeling "down," but we can also lose hope that things will turn around. This starts a belief structure that will make it harder to turn your emotional state around.

But it is also your choice to take positive actions that will shift brain control and change the type of hormones that are secreted and the resulting emotions. There is always hope, generated by a conscious decision to focus on the positive.

Mantras, such as the ones listed below, are a great first step to a turn-around. Pick a positive version of the challenge you're experiencing and say it over and over – even if you don't believe it at first.

As you focus on the meaning of the mantra, you shift brain control into the frontal lobe. This limits the reflex brain production of negative emotions. As you continue to use a cognitive strategy, you gain control over your actions, which stimulates positive emotions.

In a recent race, I was running up a long hilly section with a group when one of the runners started whining about the hill. When another runner echoed the negative thought, I had heard enough. I said to the group, "Repeat after me . . . WE LOVE HILLS." For the next few miles of this uphill course, during the running portion, we made quite a statement repeating our positive mantra over and over. It worked! I didn't hear any whining for rest of that marathon.

By putting some energy and commitment into the mantra, you can focus on your belief in your statement. The affirmative action reduces the negative hormones. As you say something positive, you'll produce positive hormones, which will only increase as you move from one positive act to another. Believing in your statements will help you format the reflex brain to shift in a positive mode more automatically.

Get out and run today, and get positive about life!

Mantras that can turn emotions in a positive direction

(Feel free to use these or create your own)

- I'm going to get moving — I'll feel good!

- I'm moving!

- I know I can do this!

- I'm feeling better!

- I love endorphins!

- I'm changing my attitude!

- I feel better!

- I feel good!

- I feel light!

- Feeling positive!

- I can do it!

32 I have a date with a 5K (10K) on my calendar, and I must prepare

Deadlines can get you motivated, whether it's 5K, 10K, or a run around the block with a child or friend. The studies show that when a goal is written on a calendar, there are more running days per month resulting in a higher level of fitness.

The cognitive act of choosing a race and writing it down activates the frontal lobe. As you look at the calendar and review your training schedule, you'll use this executive brain, taking control away from your subconscious reflex brain.

This reduces the chance that stress will cause negative attitude hormones to be released. But if they are, you can focus on the goal, go through the plan, and keep regaining control over the process.

Each race is a reward, and I'm not talking about the goodies after the race. Finishing in a stream of people is invigorating. If you could bottle the energy from a race, you could power your car for a year. The mood is upbeat, people are nice, and why wouldn't they be this way: they're doing something positive to improve the quality of their health, vitality, and their mental attitude.

Those who enter races tend to be more regular with their training, both leading up to the race and afterward. The motivation boost can last for months.

© Pixland/Thinkstock

Before you run the first race, schedule and enter your next one. If you wait to enter, you are more likely to lose focus. In this way, you can move from one upbeat event to the next, year-round.

Fill out that entry now, and you're on your way!

How to select a race

If it's your first race, look for one that is fun:

- Festive

- Good refreshments

- T-shirt and other goodies

- Entertainment

- The organizers focus on average or beginning runners

- Well organized – The organizers keep things in order: accurate measurement, accurate timing (usually using "the chip" technology), no long lines, easy to register, start goes off on time, water on the course, refreshments for all – even the slowest should have no major problems

- Competitive runners like the event and respect the organizers.

Resources: Where to find out about races

- Running stores – Ask for fun events

- Friends who run – Get the opinions

- Running clubs – Do a web search "running clubs (your town)"

- Newspaper listings – Weekend edition or online

- Web Searches – Just do a web search for "road races (your town)" or "5K (your town)."

How to register

- Online – More and more road running events are conducting registration online. This allows you to bypass the process of finding an entry form and sending it in before the deadline.

- Fill out an entry and send it in (with a check) or pay online.

- Show up on race day – Because some races don't do race day registration, be sure you can do this. There is usually a penalty for waiting until the last minute, but you can see what the weather is like before you make the trek to the race.

© Ryan McVay/Digital Vision/Thinkstock

33 I want to finish a Marathon or Half Marathon

Crossing the finish line in a long race is an empowering experience that changes lives for the better. Many famous and accomplished movie stars, scientists, doctors, and statesmen have said that the achievement they are most proud of is the training for and completion of a 26.2-mile or 13.1-mile event.

There are many variables in training and finishing a race. During at least one run a week, the motivation must be found to get up and out the door. During several crucial runs in the training season, the inner strength must be found to keep going. During several sections of the race itself, the willpower is tested, and the runner must dig down and find hidden strengths. Most runners – even beginners – find that they have a deep source of hidden strength that pulls them through.

Many runners can bluff their way through a 5K or even a 10K. But most who train for the long events know that severe consequences occur to those who don't do the minimum training as noted in my books *Galloway Training Programs* and *Year Round Plan*. Therefore, most who really want to finish the race do the training. The date on the calendar is a powerful motivator to get the workout done on that day.

There's no need to be injured or out of commission during a marathon or half training program. When walk breaks are taken often enough, and rest days are inserted as needed, the body rebuilds and adapts to the gradual increase in distance.

Each successive long run bestows an amazing sense of personal achievement. This momentum almost always ensures that the two short runs are done during the week. Each long run pushes one closer to the goal.

Those who have a significant goal, like a marathon or half, tend to watch their diet and other lifestyle habits. They tend to eat less junk food, make healthier choices, sleep well, and enjoy a positive mental attitude.

Those who complete a 5-6 month Galloway training program have a 95% chance of continuing to run for the next year. Those who run for a year have a 90% chance of becoming life-long runners. This mission changes lives for the better.

Sign up now — make the commitment!

Minimum for finishing a Marathon or Half Marathon: 3 days per week

1. THE LONG RUN. A long run every 2-3 weeks that gradually increases to 14 miles for the half and 26 miles for the marathon. The pace should be at least 2 min/mi slower than one could currently run in a marathon as noted by the "magic mile" listed on page 139. Slow the long runs by 30 sec/mi for every 5F temperature increase above 60F.

2. MAGIC MILE. Run several strategic "magic mile" time trials as noted in the schedules in the books below.

3. Insert liberal walk breaks into all long runs. Walk break frequency will increase as the pace slows and the temperature increases.

4. Minimum amount of "maintenance" running days per week is three, usually Tuesday, Thursday and one of the weekend days. Tuesday and Thursday could be 30 minutes each. On non-long-run weekends, the minimum is 60 minutes.

Resource Books (available at www.jeffgalloway.com)

- *Half Marathon*
- *Marathon – You Can Do It*
- *Year Round Plan*
- *Galloway Training Programs*

34 When I can't make a decision, I run

Decisions often build up stress, which trigger anxiety hormones and then negative attitude hormones. It's ironic that when you really need a good run to help you sort through decision issues, you often aren't motivated to run. You can turn this situation around in a few minutes.

Play a game with yourself that you're only going to run for 5 minutes. Get out the door! Maintain a slow pace. If you run too fast for that day, you'll add to the stress, which will interfere with much of the decision-making process.

At first, I'm going so slowly that there is no huffing and puffing. I'm enjoying moving forward, feeling the exertion of the legs, the muscles, and the heart and lungs. During each walk break, the endorphins lock in and the attitude improves. This also activates the frontal lobe, which is the executive brain.

The left side of this uniquely human brain logically identifies the underlying problems in making a decision. Next, this logical center will break down each problem into manageable issues, with a rough concept of each problem.

Logic can only go so far in making difficult decisions. That activity takes place on the left side of the frontal lobe. To shift gears, I'll re-focus for a while on the rhythm of my steps, on what's going on around me: the trees, the clouds, the people, the other animals. When we are playful, the body and mind relax.

My short "recess break" allows me the chance to shift into the right side of the frontal lobe. This center of creativity has innovation and intuition that can unlock the locked-up logic. It subconsciously makes connections and comes up with creative solutions time after time.

Again, the pace must be slow to lower stress so that the right side can work its magic. Faster running builds up stress, which tends to shut off the free-flowing action of this creative/intuitive powerhouse.

So the left side sets up the issues and breaks them into manageable pieces. It also formats the key problems. This allows the right brain to work on solutions or find inner resources to "face up to it" or "dig down deeper."

The decision may not be clear by the end of the run, but there's a new sense of confidence. I almost always finish the run feeling that a decision can be made. Without the shifting of mental action to the frontal lobe during the run, I am sure that many of my decisions would not have been made as soon or as well.

Setting up a decision-making run

- Run slowly – The frontal lobe is activated by running, but too much stress reduces effectiveness
- Get into a rhythm – Provides structure, stimulation and positive environment for both left and right brain activity
- Have a mantra – Oriented around the decision
- Laugh and smile – Opens up the positive hormones and right brain activity
- Take a good, lower lung breath, every 3rd or 4th breath
- Think of the key issues and say "I can do it" 3-5 times, regularly
- Enjoy every minute of your run
- Relax and let the right brain sort things out

35 Turning a negative into your positive: Hills, strong wind, rain

Let's be honest, most runners don't like to face adverse conditions. The reflex brain anticipates stress from these conditions and will stimulate the production of anxiety hormones and then negative ones.

On bad days, the good news is that you will have a huge competitive advantage if you accept the challenge and believe that you will compete better. It's fine to bluff your way through.

Mental training and preparation are key. Setting up rehearsal plans, such as those in my book Mental Training, can pull you through hilly courses/rain/snow/wind and help you face a variety of tough situations in life.

In each rehearsal, you are taking cognitive action to prepare and then you are taking conscious control on the days you're faced with the challenges. This stops the flow of negative attitude peptides and stimulates the production of positive ones.

By facing adversity, you desensitize yourself to it. The actual stress on the body is minimal. The reflex brain tries to steer you into pleasure and away from discomfort. This subconscious entity simply monitors stress and triggers low motivation and negative attitude hormones when the level rises a bit too high. Each time you run in adverse conditions, you strengthen your toughness attitude circuits, which can be activated to turn attitudes around.

On long runs, be realistic. If it is below 32F (0 C) and rainy, you will have to evaluate the misery index. With appropriate clothing, you can be fine, but be prepared.

Start with 5 minutes. The first 5 minutes in the cold, the wind, and the rain are the most miserable. Once out there, you will realize that you are going to be fine. Even if you don't feel wonderful, you will get used to facing the challenge and will probably go farther the next time.

Break the run into segments with "adjustment breaks." When it's cold and/or rainy, adjust layers with 5-minute warm-up breaks. During hot weather, take a 5-minute "cold shower break." Run in different directions when it's windy.

Hint: On a cold windy day, run into the wind during the first half of the run.

Running against the wind

On a windy race day, someone around you is going to say something like "I hate wind." Without thinking, tell yourself, "I run my best races when it's windy." Then smile. Immediately you will gain control over your actions by using the executive brain in the frontal lobe. This allows you to pick a positive idea and focus on it for a few moments, then pick another positive thought.

As you continue to make positive statements out loud, you are changing your thinking process from a reactive mode (letting the reflex brain take subconscious action) to planning and taking action using the conscious human brain. This allows you to focus on the positive. Positive attitude hormones are being produced.

Using mantras stimulates more positive hormones as you run into the wind, rain, up a hill, etc. Practice various mantras during your training runs and have them ready on race day. As you continue to repeat the mantra, you develop a belief in your positive actions and gain more and more confidence.

You must take conscious control over the physical side of your effort also. As you run into a strong wind during a race, or up a hill, you should be shortening your stride, maintaining effort level, and taking the appropriate walk breaks to let the legs recover for the next segment.

When your competitors hear you embrace the challenge and confront it, many will psychologically give the racing edge to you. Being positive builds self-respect and respect among other runners.

Who knows, you may come out of the race with a true love of the wind against your face, the power of overcoming adversity, and the belief that you actually love running in the wind.

Chapter 3
I run for rewards

© iStockphoto/Thinkstock

36 To feel the bounce of a new pair of shoes

There's something special about running in a new pair of shoes that you really like. I've been running in the Mizuno Wave Rider model for about 8 years and love the shoe. It feels like an extension of my foot as I run: the shoe and the foot are working together as a team to move me down the road.

Many runners are motivated to run because they have invested in a shoe that works for their foot. Shoes today can protect a foot that needs protection and help a foot move through the running motion more smoothly. All major companies are continuing to research how to make running shoes work better for the individual foot.

The first reward in buying a new pair of running shoes is the knowledge you'll gain from being fitted by an experienced staff person in a technical running store. For about 40 years, my Phidippides store in Atlanta has had an ongoing training course for staff members about how the foot operates and which shoes are best for certain ranges of motion. We match up the customer with several shoes and allow each to choose which one fits better while giving advice and answering questions.

Running stores are not equal in service. Only a few have these two key characteristics:

1. staff members who are thoroughly knowledgeable about running shoes and foot mechanics; and

2. a training course for each employee to teach the science and art of fitting running shoes/foot issues.

Another reward is the reduction of aches and pains when running with a shoe that is matched up with your foot. Some aches can occur when the shoe is too broken down. The right shoe, with the right features, can make you feel that you're not having to work as hard.

Caution: Don't wait until an old shoe is worn out. I hear of several injuries every year that are caused by moving from a worn out shoe to one that is too rigid in its correction. When in doubt, ask the most experienced staff person for an opinion about how to break in the new pair, etc.

In the sidebar below, you'll find a proven way to tell when it is time to switch. There are also suggestions for avoiding the dramatic shift from old to new pair.

Phidippides.com shoe tip
When should you change shoes?

Mileage figures vary with individuals and at different periods of training. Here is a proven way to know when it's best to shift to a newer pair of shoes.

1. When you find a shoe that works, get a second pair, right away. Companies adjust their models every few months and if you wait too long, your favorite shoe will probably be significantly changed. Ask the store staff if the shoe you are getting is the exact one you purchased. Sometimes the same shoe is made in several different factories, in different countries.

2. Walk around in your new pair for an hour or two every day. This allows your feet to "mold to the insole" and reduces break-in issues.

3. Alternate shoes during one run each week. When you have 1-2 miles left in the designated run, on a short day, put on the newer pair. This will gradually break in the new shoe without causing excessive wear.

4. When the old one starts to lose its support, use the new one. When the original pair is at the end of its support life, you will notice a significant difference in the two shoes. Before there is a huge difference in support, make the shift. At that point, use the old one for yard work, etc.

5. Go back to the store and get your next backup pair.

6. Start breaking in a new pair.

37 I'm running so I can take the family to Disney World

There are some sacrifices that family members make when runners are running for hours and hours on the long runs – why not reward them? A woman told me recently that during the early part of her marathon training program, when her grandkids wanted her to do something on a long run day, she would say the following: "I'm getting into shape so that I can take you to a special place." This calmed them down for several weeks.

The curiosity started building so she gave them a date that was about a month before the event when she would make her announcement. This also settled down the questions for a while. On the big day, she had a little surprise party for the grandchildren. As they walked into the house, there was a mascot toy for each child as they walked toward the den. Surrounded by theme posters and decorations, came the big announcement: Since everyone had been so patient with her preparing for her big race day, she was going to reward everyone . . . "We're going to Disney World!"

A growing number of parents/grandparents choose a goal race in an area where kids and adults can enjoy themselves. Some go to exotic destinations like Athens, Greece to run the "original" marathon course or to Rome, Italy. Others pick a U.S. event where there are interesting sites, like the Big Sur International Marathon in California.

The most popular destinations for marathoners and half marathoners among the runners I've heard from are the Disney venues of Disney World and Disneyland. There is something for everyone. There are events for all ages, and it's common to have three generations running in, say the Disney Princess Half Marathon, Epcot Wine & Dine Half, or the Disney World Marathon. Many family members start running by entering a 5K associated with each event. Non-runners can find lots of fun activities also.

My kids were 9 and 11 when we went to our first Disney World Marathon. They were excited about the trip and kept talking about it for months. It's been about two decades now and the Galloways have recorded perfect attendance at the Disney events. Two decades later, our "kids" want to be there every year also.

Note: Go to www.runDisney.com for information on all of these magical events.

38 I'll reward myself with a new outfit

Rewards work! Positive reinforcement helps us stay motivated. When you give yourself a functional garment that will help you during your runs, the benefits increase.

Set a goal that is realistic but meaningful: finishing all of the long runs through the first half of a marathon/half training program or finishing a significant workout such as the last long run before the race.

Look at the technical garments that could help you during the rest of the season – or during the race itself. The staff members in a technical running store can help. Tell the running store techie what you are looking for and ask to see the options. You will receive an education on the latest fibers for various conditions.

Cold days: Many technical fibers keep you warm but are not very thick. They also tend to release excess heat buildup, should this occur. This allows you to have one layer on many winter days, with additional layers as needed. The Mizuno "breath thermo" fiber actually warms up as you perspire. So instead of getting chilly on cold days when wet, it's possible to stay comfortable.

Hot days: Light microfiber fabrics can keep you cooler. These allow for better evaporation to reduce the effects of the heat during the summer whether the moisture comes from perspiration or water that you pour on yourself.

Precipitation days: Modern technical fibers will tend to hold very little moisture and release it. Many of the latest garments wick the moisture away from the skin, providing warmth next to the body.

Reward for completing the goal – Choose something that will help you continue running after the goal is achieved. This is when you can get yourself a matching outfit that you really want to wear. Many runners choose a garment with the logo of the race they finished – worn with pride!

Note: The "clothing thermometer" in the following books will guide you for dressing at various temperatures: *Running Until You're 100, Half Marathon, 5K/10K*, and *A Woman's Guide to Running*.

39 I run for chocolate

I've heard from hundreds of runners who used chocolate as a reward for doing the tough runs or getting through a full week of training. It's possible to eat chocolate daily and lose both fat and weight during a training program. The secret is to budget for the calories and have a system for managing portion control.

Budgets shift us into the conscious brain so that we can control our eating and avoid subconscious reflex eating behaviors. Budgeting for foods you love is better than prohibition.

Many chocolate-loving runners, under the spell of a New Year's resolution, will mistakenly try to totally abstain from chocolate (which sets up a "starvation reflex"). They often hold out for several weeks, but when the "banned substance" is available and no one is around, one bite leads to a reflex eating binge, aggravated by deprivation.

Chocolate, ice cream, and potato chips are only some of the foods that trigger subconscious reflex eating patterns. Certain combinations of sugar, salt, and fat trigger the release of dopamine, a powerful neurotransmitter hormone that locks into receptor sites giving us a really good pleasurable "hit" for a few seconds after we consume it. Most of us have had experiences with these foods as children and became quickly hardwired for subconscious eating patterns. We eat a piece of chocolate and feel good, so subconsciously we reach for and eat another and another. Because this is patterned in the reflex brain and is subconscious, we can consume a great quantity in a short time period without any concept of how many calories have been consumed.

Barbara Galloway, in *A Woman's Guide to Fatburning*, offers a proven way to have your chocolate and fat control, too. First, put yourself on a calorie budget for the day. If you really want or need a chocolate reward on that day, select the portion of chocolate that will fit into the budget and adjust other foods accordingly.

Your run will not only add to the burning side of the equation, but it will increase the eating budget. Do your run and earn the chocolate. Good disciplined work should be rewarded. By "doing the math" and tabulating the calories allowed, you shift mental control to the strategic frontal lobe where you can maintain control over the dopamine reflex eating patterns triggered by the subconscious brain.

Get out and run — then think yourself into a reward snack!

Note: Read more about the calorie budget on page 160.

40 I run for wine

Wine has been a healthy reward at the end of a Mediterranean day for thousands of years. The Greeks have cultivated grapes for wine for over 9,000 years, according to experts. Phidippides (the marathon messenger in 490BC) and his fellows probably relaxed at the end of a long running journey with their mature grape juice of choice.

For those high-energy folks who don't have alcoholic risk factors, a daily glass or two before bed may facilitate getting to sleep. Daily consumption of alcohol has been shown to reduce the risk of heart disease and certain cancers. As in many of life's choices, the key to managing alcohol consumption is moderation.

By exercising portion control, we accomplish more than avoiding alcohol excess. Setting our limit and cognitively monitoring it will activate the frontal lobe of the brain. This can override the subconscious reflex brain, which will trigger repetitive consumption of alcohol without realizing the amount.

The hormones triggered by alcohol stimulate the reflex brain to grab another glass – and then another. You break this reflex behavior by monitoring each drink and accounting for it in your calorie budget for the day.

Wine had a role in the first marathon race, during the 1896 Athens Olympics. A first-hand report noted that vineyards along the course offered wine to the participants. The reporter did not mention how much was consumed. I have a feeling that the officials appreciated this more than the athletes.

The Medoc Marathon in France runs through vineyards that allow wine tasting along the course. I've heard stories that several participants didn't make it past the second wine stop.

I suppose that these "researchers" wanted to make sure that the taste was as good as they thought on the first sip. One runner told me that the taste kept getting better.

Even those who want to burn fat can enjoy a glass or two. Again, the key is to account for each ounce in the calorie budget for the day and set a limit.

In that way, runners can take responsibility and enjoy an ancient lifestyle beverage.

41 My story: I ran for ice cream

During the two-year period, before the 1972 Olympic Trials, I ramped up my mileage from 80 to 140 miles a week. With each increase, I was hungry but had trouble finding foods that would digest easily when running 2 or 3 workouts a day. Then I discovered chocolate chip mint flavored ice cream.

Since I was training in the warm climate of Tallahassee, FL, there was a slight cooling effect after eating it. Between workouts I could eat a bowl or two, replace my calories and not have digestive problems during the next workout.

OK, some of this was a rationalization because I loved the taste. But my energy level was stable and I didn't have to interrupt my workouts for bathroom stops. On some days, I ate practically nothing but half a gallon of the mint-flavored product.

When Barbara and I were married, she joined me in having an ice cream reward almost every night. We were running a lot, and it was the reward we gave ourselves for reaching mileage goals for that day, which kept the fat from accumulating.

Then, on a fateful New Year's day, we decided to eliminate the chocolate chip mint ice cream from our diet — after more than 10 years of enjoyment. We were successful for two years. A leftover box after a birthday party got us re-started on the habit, and we even increased our intake over what it had been before due to having deprived ourselves.

You can "starve" yourself of a food that you dearly love for an extended period of time. But at some time in the future, when the food is around and no one else is, you will tend to over-consume that food. My correction for this problem was the following:

- I made a contract with myself: I could have a little of it whenever I wanted – while promising to be "reasonable."

- Setting a goal of enjoying one bowl a week, 5 years from now.

- Four years from now, enjoying a bowl every 5 days.

- Three years from now, a bowl every 4 days.

- Learning to enjoy healthy sweet things, like fruit salads, energy bars, etc., as replacements.

It worked! I hardly ever eat any ice cream but sometimes enjoy a bowl if I want. This is purely for medicinal reasons, you understand.

42 Reward: A running retreat or running school

Imagine a week or a weekend during which you didn't have to work. Days were spent running, meeting good people, eating, sleeping, and learning. In addition, you find yourself motivated for months afterward. This is the essence of what we do during our Galloway running retreats.

Many of our participants tell me that the retreat was their reward for staying with their running program for 3 months, 6 months, a year. Others needed a motivation boost after a layoff.

Several times a year, Barbara and I conduct beach weekend retreats at Blue Mountain Beach, FL. Not only is there a beautiful white sand beach, but due to its location, there is a series of state parks and a forest preserve, which means hundreds of miles of beautiful trails that wind through pine forests.

Usually during the middle of July, we conduct a weeklong program in the Lake Tahoe area of California. During each retreat, there are clinics on building endurance, nutrition, fat-burning, getting faster, motivation, shoes, strength, and more. Individual questions are asked constantly, and problem-solving situations are welcomed. Interacting with others results in new friendships and a lot of fun. Joy Johnson is one of our long-term friends who inspires us every year. She has won her age group many times in the Boston and New York marathons. But that's not the main source of inspiration. Last year, while on a hike, Joy slipped and hurt her leg so badly that she didn't know that she would be able to run again. When one is over 80, the healing is much slower, but Joy was determined. One year later, Joy was back at Tahoe, training for the next marathon. She is also a beautiful person with a lot of determination.

Each participant can receive an individualized running form evaluation. Suggestions are given for those who have challenges. Several form drills are taught to help improve running mechanics.

Running schools are 3-hour to 5-hour focused sessions that cover the content areas taught at running retreats. These are held in about 20 locations around the U.S. each year.

During each session, I can cut through the conflicting advice, help design a focused training program, and deal with individual problems. I personally conduct each of these sessions.

Sign up now and you'll be motivated leading up to the retreat/school, with a boost for months afterward.

43 My run earns me a special snack

There's something very satisfying about the after-run snack. You've paid your dues and now you're rewarded. For millions of years, our ancestors walked and ran to gather food and were rewarded when they could eat. The sensation of

© Brand X/Thinkstock

satisfaction was more than just the food gratification. The symbol of success and accomplishment was the reward meal.

Top priority in your body organism is the production of energy to keep the body moving. Exercise turns on the energy circuits and gets them ready to reload. For millions of years, our ancestors needed to be ready to keep moving at all times, to find food/shelter, and get away from predators. This fine-tuned energy replacement mechanism kept the fuel flowing to muscles and especially to the brain. We have inherited all of these capabilities.

Eating within half an hour after a run will help reload energy stores for the next run. When you choose the right snack and consume it within 30 minutes of finishing, you can replace the glycogen (stored carbohydrates) needed for the first 30 minutes of your next workout. Based upon research on reloading, the recommended ratio of nutrients is 80% simple carbs/20% protein. The products Accelerade and Endurox R4 have this in their mix.

The longer you run, the more reward calories you can consume. After a 3-miler or less, about 100 calories are needed. When you run 4-11 miles, you can consume 150 to 200 calories. A snack of 250 calories is recommended for those who have run 12-20 miles. After running 20 miles or more, it's best to have a 300-calorie snack.

If you reload 30 minutes after exercise, you may reduce your hunger later in the day. Running uses up some of the brain's reserve fuel, glycogen. Since the reflex brain monitors crucial fuel levels closely, it knows when the stock has not been restored and will subconsciously trigger a hunger response. Reloading tends to reduce or eliminate this.

If you are trying to burn off fat, you will be helping yourself by consuming this reloading snack within that first half hour. So run and eat with no guilt, but account for it in your calorie budget.

44 Running allows me to enjoy my music even better

The primitive origins of music and dance occurred during the long treks made by ancient ancestors on foot, according to experts. Spending 15 hours or more per day on foot embedded in the subconscious brain a rhythm based on certain patterns of steps. This led to beating patterns on logs, hollow plants, and then drums.

Then cadence voice sounds evolved, followed by chants, then songs and dance. And it all started during the early Paleolithic era by ancestors responding to the walking/running rhythm of the feet during the constant daily movement.

© jean-marie guyon/iStockphoto/Thinkstock

With the many downloads available, it's possible to record a series of songs that have a specific beat when one wants to run at a certain pace. I have put together a training app for 5K and 10K that includes music (see lolofit.com, the Galloway Ultimate 5K or 10K). Half marathon and marathon apps are in the works also. When the pace of the workout picks up, so does the beat of the music.

Even if you don't listen to music during a run that might be a bit boring, you can make up your own chant or cadence. This will get you into the frontal lobe and may trigger some creative and entertaining messages from the right side of the human brain.

At the very least, you can have fun and laugh. This releases positive hormones that can turn a so-so run into a good run. It can also make a good run into a great run. Again, you can take control over your attitude.

It's OK to feel like you're dancing down the road.

Downloads for entertainment or improvement

Lolofit: I recorded the instructions for daily workouts, with tips, leading to the following events:

The Galloway Ultimate 5K Training Program

The Galloway Ultimate 10K Training Program

Coming . . . Half Marathon and Marathon

RunKeeper:

Galloway 5K training app

Galloway Half Marathon app

MotionTrax:

Music with walk breaks

Free: 30-second run/30 -econds walk

Free: run a minute/walk a minute

Also, for a fee:

Run 2 min/walk 1 min

Run 3 min/walk 1 min

Podcast: The Galloway Extra Mile Podcast (free)

This podcast is produced and directed by Kevin Gwin. During several episodes, Kevin and I work together to explain and highlight the components of my training in the sequence of a training season.

Chapter 4
I run to erase stress

45 Stressed? Get out and run!

On the really stressful days, when we don't feel like running, even a short and gentle run can deliver major relief. Running doesn't just release stress, it can bestow a relaxed sense of confidence that allows one to meet the challenges that cause the stress.

Your subconscious (reflex) brain monitors stress. When this powerful management component determines that the level is too high, it subconsciously triggers anxiety hormones and then negative attitude secretions to reduce motivation. These internally produced mood drugs lock into receptor sites all over the body, tuning down the energy level and attitude. If you don't take action to reduce stress and add to the overload, depressive hormones can be produced.

© Pixland/Thinkstock

Good news! By using a number of cognitive strategies, you can shift control away from the subconscious reflex brain and into the frontal lobe. This is the brain that humans have and animals don't. This conscious entity can take control over the situation and override the subconscious brain. You don't have to eliminate the stress to reduce the negative attitude secretions.

By consciously acknowledging that stress is the reason for this situation, you'll shift to the executive center, the frontal lobe. By designing a strategy in this conscious brain, you'll not only shift control away from the reflex brain and reduce negative hormone production. By moving yourself through a series of positive cognitive actions, you can reprogram the reflex brain.

Several mental drills are provided in my book *Mental Training*, which can be designed specifically for the individual challenge. Each drill is a cognitive strategy that shifts you into the conscious brain. As you use each of these regularly, you can reprogram the reflex brain to the behavior pattern you wish, such as getting out the door on a tough day.

Promise yourself one thing on a stressful day: that you will do 5 minutes of running (or run/walk/run). Once you are running, you'll tend to run for half an hour, which can recharge your good attitude. But even if you only do 5 minutes, you'll knock the stress level down a notch or two.

A short run on a stressed-out day gives you more control over your attitude, and therefore your ability to deal with stress.

Control stress, step by step. Get moving!

46 A morning run gets me awake, alive, and ready for the day

Thousands of runners have told me that just the thought of morning exercise used to be very stressful. A growing number have found that a morning run gets the body and mind ready for the day, while reducing stress.

After a cup or two of coffee, there's nothing that feels better to me than moving down the road or trail early in the morning. Body and mind wake up together, as the spirit rises, minute by minute, walk break by walk break.

Slow moving brains get a boost from the special energy of the new day. Easing into the run brings the glow of blood flow to muscles, joints, feet, and the brain. With each step, adaptations are made, hormones are secreted, and your system as a whole "wakes up."

Running activates the frontal lobe, warming it up for the day. This conscious brain is "in the moment," processing the route, the exertion level, making form adjustments. It's always better to go slower early in a morning run to avoid the stress of huffing and puffing.

When running at a comfortable pace, the brain rehearses problems and projects ahead, generating solutions and entertaining images. Running too fast puts stress on the brain, triggering anxiety and then negative attitude hormones.

Step by step, the rhythm of the feet is comfortable and reassuring. For millions of years, our ancestors set this pattern and everything warms up when we go with the flow.

We're in the moment, enjoying the new day.

Getting out the door early in the morning

The most common motivational problem, as presented to me by runners, is how to get out of bed early enough and be ready to do a long run, hard workout, race, or simply a run that was assigned for that day.

State your desired outcome: To be awake and fully engaged in the run, from the start.

Detail the challenge: Desire to lie in bed, no desire to exert yourself so early. The stress of the alarm clock and having to think about what to do next when the brain isn't working very well.

Break up the challenge into a series of actions, which lead you through the mental barriers, no one of which is challenging to the reflex brain.

- The night before, lay out your running clothes and shoes (often near the coffee machine) so that you don't have to think.

- Set your alarm, and as you are laying in bed, say to yourself over and over: ALARM OFF . . . FEET ON FLOOR . . . TO THE KITCHEN. Or, simply stated:

- ALARM . . . FEET . . . KITCHEN

- As you repeat this, visualize doing each action without thinking. By repeating it, you lull yourself to sleep. You have also been programming yourself to take action the next morning.

- The alarm goes off. You shut it off, put your feet on the floor, and head to the kitchen – all without thinking – because you programmed the reflex brain to do this.

- You're putting on one piece of clothing at a time, sipping coffee (tea, diet cola, etc.), never thinking about exercise.

- With coffee cup in hand and clothes on, you stick your head out the door to see what the weather is like.

- Driving to the workout or race, sipping your beverage, you rehearse seeing friends, feeling the positive energy of an event, easing into the workout/race, feeling good about your exertion.

- OR, you walk to the edge of your property, put the coffee cup down, and cross the street. You're on your way.

- The endorphins are kicking in. The positive peptides are rising, you feel good, and you want to continue.

Principle of motivational physics: A body on the bed wants to stay on the bed. But once a body is in motion, it wants to stay in motion.

Note: For more information, see my book *Mental Training*, available at www.jeffgalloway.com.

47 A noontime run erases morning stress and clears the head

I believe that when you run at noon you can be more productive at work during the afternoon. Even a short run at midday allows the brain to reset itself, while boosting attitude and energy level.

© Comstock Images/Thinkstock

There are logistic issues: Do you have/need a shower? Do you have enough time during your lunch break? Is there a health club available with a treadmill in case of bad weather? How will you arrange for your lunch?

Once you deal with these issues, run out the door! A major amount of stress that has been building up, especially during an overloaded day, can be released by the noon run. Even 15 to 20 minutes can clean out a lot of the garbage. At the same time, even a short run can energize the brain and get it ready to focus during the afternoon.

Once the benefits are realized, runners tend to look forward to their noontime vitality boost. Just the knowledge that the run was scheduled can calm stress buildup during the morning.

Some runners make this a second run, running either in the morning or after work. If you get a chance, inject yourself with mental and physical energy with a short "recess run."

Quick noontime workouts

1. Out and back. Walk for 1-2 minutes to get to your running course, jog slowly for 2 minutes. Then run in a direction where you are unlikely to have cross streets or other interruptions. Turn around after 6-10 minutes. Take a one-minute walk break and then try to run back a little faster.

2. 2-minute to 3-minute drill. Whether on a treadmill or running outdoors, time yourself for 2 or 3 minutes (your choice). Walk for a minute between segments. Run the first segment gently, the second segment a bit faster, and the third segment fairly fast. Don't sprint. If you have time, keep adding segments.

3. Hill challenge. Walk and jog slowly to a medium or easy hill, about 100 walking steps in length. Start each hill at a jog and gradually pick up the cadence or turnover of the feet as you go up by shortening your stride. Go down to baby steps if needed. It's OK to be huffing and puffing a bit at the top, but don't sprint. Walk down the hill for recovery. Start with two hills and build up to 5-8 of them for added strength and hill technique.

4. One more minute. Walk for 1-2 minutes and then jog very easily for a minute. Then time yourself for one minute running a little faster than the warm-up, but fairly easy, and then walk for 30 seconds. If you want to speed up, pick up the pace a little on each one-minute run, but don't sprint. It's also fine to just stay at a comfortable pace. Run as many of these as you wish.

© Ryan McVay/Digital Vision/Thinkstock

48 An evening run
erases the stress of the day

There's nothing like a run to erase stress and settle the mind to enjoy the evening. Many afternoon/evening runners don't feel like running. Agitated by the complications of the day's work, they usually force themselves out the door. After 3-5 minutes, the problems aren't so bad. By 15 minutes, there's a comfortable feeling settling into various parts of the body and mind. Even those who run for a total of 15 minutes after work tell me that they are able to relax better at home.

Gentle runs, with strategic walk breaks, deliver a continuing flow of positive attitude hormones called endorphins. Recognized as the most positive attitude boosting substances the body produces, endorphins lock into receptor sites in billions of cells throughout the body and mind. This sends positive attitude messages throughout the system.

You feel better and better, as long as you have the right pace and a balance in running and walking. When running continuously, the endorphins are primarily used to kill pain in weak links and heavily worked muscles. During the walk breaks, there's no running pain to kill, so the endorphins can inject their "feeling good" messages throughout the system.

It's best to maintain a gentle pace when you want to unwind after a busy day. This allows the right side of your frontal lobe to find the right rhythm of the feet and legs, and keep everything going. Monitor breathing rate and avoid huffing and puffing.

The gentle rhythm of the feet triggers a number of positive actions in your circuits sending energy, relaxing the muscles, and getting you ready for the rest of the day. Positive attitude hormones are secreted as you flow with the rhythm. This is enhanced by chanting or singing to the cadence.

Some runners find that running from the office lets the rush hour traffic calm down for a much quicker commute home. Those who live near their work can run home if there is a safe route.

Two of the primary challenges in getting motivated after work are low blood sugar and low metabolism. By having an energy bar and a cup of coffee, tea, etc., about 30-45 minutes before the run, most of those issues can be managed.

Getting out the door after work, school, or a tough day

Many runners must run in the afternoon but commonly feel drained at the end of the day. This is another instance of the reflex brain responding to the stress of the day, often due to low blood sugar, which triggers negative peptides that leave you feeling tired and unmotivated.

State your desired outcome: To get out the door and be running down the road.

Detail the challenge: Stress-induced negative mood hormones that result in a negative attitude, desire to sit on the couch or take a nap. The thought of a workout is stressful, which can trigger more negative secretions and negative messages.

Reduce stress as you are driving or walking home by saying, "I'm going to get home, put on some comfortable clothes and eat and drink." This reduces stress in several ways. There is no thought given to running, and even the thought of eating and drinking can stimulate positive peptides.

- Put on some comfortable clothes and shoes – they just happen to be running attire.
- Eat an energy snack (easily digestible) and drink water or a caffeinated beverage (if OK with you). Caffeine can shift mood very effectively.
- Think relaxing thoughts
- Stick your head out the door to check the weather
- Walk around outside to see what's going on
- Cross the street, and you're on your way

Principle of lazy physics: A body on the couch wants to stay on the couch. But once a body is in motion, it wants to stay in motion.

Break up the challenge into a series of actions that lead you through the mental barriers, no one of which is challenging to the reflex brain.

Chapter 5
I run to improve and feel better

49 I run so that I can glide

By using efficient running form, you can feel smoother on every run. The secret is to reduce the running motion to a simple and gentle movement pattern. By focusing on the principles below and doing a few energizing drills, you can teach yourself to run easier and faster.

Running is a natural motion for the human body. As you run regularly, your right brain subconsciously searches for more efficient patterns. Studies show that runners get smoother as they continue to run regularly.

Trying to mimic someone or force a certain running technique on oneself will usually result in aches, pains, and/or injuries. Many of these problems surface when runners try something they read in an article or imitate someone faster than they are. The best form for you is that which follows your natural range of motion.

Here are the general principles of efficient running form:

- Feet low to the ground

- Relatively short range of motion and short stride

- Light touch of the foot

- Generally upright body posture

If one naturally leans forward, then this is fine. Be aware that a forward lean can put stress on the back and/or the neck.

When the stride is naturally short enough and the feet are low to the ground, the ankle does most of the work. This will make running smoother and easier, reducing the work of the calf muscle. The cadence drill below will help you adapt naturally to an efficient use of the ankle.

You can train yourself to be a better glider by doing the acceleration-glider drill listed below.

The Acceleration-Glider Drill – sharpening mechanics and using momentum

When?

These should be done on a non-long-run day. It is fine, however, to insert them into your warm-up before a race or a speed workout. Many runners have also told me that the drills are a nice way to break up an average run that otherwise might be called "boring."

The Drill

- Done on a non-long-run day, in the middle of a shorter run, or as a warm-up for a speed session or a race or MM (magic mile) day.
- Warm up with at least half a mile of easy running.
- Many runners do the cadence drill just after the easy warm-up, followed by the acceleration-gliders. But each can be done separately, if desired.
- Run 4-8 of them.
- Do this at least once a week.
- No sprinting – never run all-out.

After teaching this drill at my one-day running schools and weekend retreats for years, I can say that most people learn better through practice when they work on the concepts listed below (rather than the details) of the drill. So just get out there and try them!

Gliding – The most important concept. This is like coasting off the momentum of a downhill run. You can do some of your gliders running down a hill if you want, but it is important to do at least two of them on the flat land.

Do this every week – As in the cadence drills, regularity is very important. If you're like most runners, you won't glide very far at first. Regular practice will help you glide farther and farther.

Here's how it's done:

- Start by jogging very slowly for about 15 steps.
- Then, jog faster for about 15 steps, increasing to a regular running pace for you.
- Now, over the next 30 steps or so, gradually increase the speed to your current race pace.
- OK, it's time to glide, or coast. Allow yourself to gradually slow down to a jog using momentum as long as you can. At first, you may glide for only 10-20 steps. As the months go by, you will get up to 30 and beyond . . . you're gliding!

Note: There's more information on running form and these drills in my books *Year Round Plan, 5K/10K, Half Marathon, Marathon: You Can Do It, and Galloway Training Programs* (available, autographed at www.jeffgalloway.com)

50　A quicker cadence picks up my spirit

Thousands of runners have told me that the one factor that "wakes them up" when they get bored or tired is increasing cadence or foot turnover. By using the cadence drill (CD) below, you can pick up the rhythm of your feet and brain.

There are thousands of sensors in the feet, legs, and brain that send signals to your subconscious reflex brain, activating established circuits to keep you running in a pattern that has worked before. After a year or two of regular running, most runners have adapted to an efficient range of motion and can run almost on "automatic pilot." It is natural to reach a state of boredom when under the influence of these circuits.

The cadence drill gently jolts the sensors and forces them to adapt. This energizes the mind-body network to make other physical changes. The first boost of energy comes from this change.

A greater energy injection comes from focusing on cadence and counting. This cognitive action shifts mental activity into the frontal lobe. The repetitive circuits of the reflex brain are overridden by the conscious brain. By shifting into the frontal lobe, you can receive another energy boost.

You'll break up the boredom by going on a mission. As you focus simply on increasing one count during each successive cadence interval, you stimulate the right brain to make the intuitive adjustments that help you run easier, lighter, and faster. By doing this for at least 4 repetitions, once or twice a week, you will format the search for efficient adaptations into the subconscious brain.

So when you are bored with an "automatic pilot" cadence, break out and increase the turnover. And when the cadence slows down at the end of a race, you will have prepared yourself to shift into a quicker turnover by doing a series of CDs.

Here's how:

© TommL/iStockphoto/Thinkstock

The Cadence Drill (CD)

When?

These should be done on a non-long run day. It is fine, however, to insert them into your warm-up, before a race or a speed workout. Many runners have also told me that the drills are a nice way to break up an average run that otherwise might be called "boring."

CD – To run smoother, lighter, and faster

This is an easy drill that helps you become a smoother runner, using less effort. By doing it regularly, you pull all the elements of good running form together at the same time. One drill a week will help you step lightly as you increase the number of steps you take per minute. This will help you run faster, with less effort.

- Warm up by walking for 5 minutes, and running and walking very gently for 10 minutes.

- Start jogging slowly for 1-2 minutes, and then time yourself for 30 seconds. During this half minute, count the number of times your left or right foot touches (pick one).

- Walk around for 20 seconds and start jogging.

- On the second 30-second drill, increase the count by 1 or 2.

- Repeat this 3-7 more times, each time trying to increase by 1-2 additional counts.

- Do this 1-2 times a week every week. If you wait two weeks between drills, you start to lose some of the adaptations

In the process of improving turnover, the body's internal monitoring system coordinates a series of adaptations that make the feet, legs, nervous system, and timing mechanism work together as an efficient team.

Note: We now have a Galloway run/walk/run timer that beeps or vibrates every 30 seconds (or the intervals of your choice) available at www.jeffgalloway.com.

51 Long runs are "health injections"

Endurance is the top benefit of running. As the long runs surpass 3 miles, 6 miles and beyond, overall stamina in life improves as does the mental toughness to deal with adversity in other areas of life.

Many internal circuits are switched "on" when we push back our current endurance limit. Research is now showing that long runs provide significant long-term health benefits:

- More blood capillaries develop in the exercising muscles for better delivery of oxygen

- The heart becomes more efficient

- Oxygen delivery is enhanced in lungs and blood system

- Mitochondria in muscle cells adapt to be better fat-burners

- Bones are either strengthened or don't tend to lose density

- Lower legs develop a smoother motion

- Feet adapt to regular forward motion exercise

- Frontal lobe solves problems, finds resources, stays active and sharp

- Mental health: Runners tend have a positive outlook and less depression

- Energy circuits are activated

- Joints adapt – runners have fewer orthopedic problems

For every hour you run, you statistically extend your life by 2-3 hours.

Let's run ourselves into better health as the years go by.

© Thomas Northcut/Photodisc/Thinkstock

How to improve endurance

1. Schedule a long run, every other week.

2. Start by running .5 to 1 mile farther than you've run in the past 2 weeks.

3. Keep increasing the long run by .5 to 1 mile every other week until you reach the distance you want to cover (or goal race distance). It's a bit better to run about a mile farther than race distance 2 weeks before the race.

4. Run 3-4 minutes per mile slower than you can run a brisk 5K pace, per mile.

5. Insert walk breaks according to the pace per mile schedule in my books listed below.

6. Maintain your basic conditioning between long runs by doing the following as a minimum:
    *   30 minutes of running on Tuesday and Thursday
    *   Build up to 60 minutes of running on the non-long-run weekend
    *   On the shorter runs, you can run at any pace, using any form of run-walk-run you wish

52 I want to keep my joints active now and 30 years from now

It may surprise you to know that runners tend to have better orthopedic units than non-runners as the decades go by. When I wrote my book *Running Until You're 100*, I compiled the studies on this issue and could not find any showing negative effects from running.

The old saying "use it or lose it" rings true. The research continues to pile up showing that if you use your joints, muscles, tendons, etc., in a natural way, without abusing them, they will continue to adapt and stay healthy.

The body is programmed to adjust and make changes based upon what you do regularly. If you run every other day, and insert the walk breaks needed for you, the orthopedic units will tend to continue adapting.

My run-walk-run method has walk breaks programmed from the beginning of a run. This provides a rest period for the joints, etc., from the stresses of running. During this break, the body repairs and replenishes a little at a time.

During my first 20 years of running, I was injured about every 20 days. Since I started taking walk breaks, over 30 years ago, I haven't had a single overuse running injury. I'm not alone. I hear from others about every day who were regularly injured until they started using the run-walk-run method from the beginning of the run. They have also avoided the return of what was, for many, regular periods of time off from running.

In *Running Until You're 100*, I showcase a number of those who are headed toward that age group and are still running a great deal. One is Don McNelly who was 85 when I interviewed him. That year, he finished 29 marathons. Don told me that his non-running friends accused him of choosing his parents well, but that was not the case: both sedentary parents had to have hip replacements in their 70s.

OK, let's move the joints and keep them in good working order!

Running and joint health

Running does not predispose joints to arthritis. Dan Wnorowski, MD, has written a paper that reviews research on the effects of running and joint health. He believes that the "majority of the relevant literature during the past decade" on this topic finds little or no basis that running increases arthritis risk. Wnorowski goes on to say that a recent MRI study indicates that the prevalence of knee meniscus abnormalities in asymptomatic marathon runners is no different than sedentary controls.

- "Studies have shown that joint nourishment is entirely based upon keeping joints in motion." Charles Jung, MD from the Group Health Cooperative website.

- "We don't see marathon runners having more joint injuries than sedentary folks. Simply put, active people have less joint injury." P.Z. Pearce, MD from Group Health Cooperative website.

- "Running offers up to 12 years protection from onset of osteoarthritis." *BBC* website 16 Oct 2002

- "Painless running or other activities which are aerobic and make you fit help keep you vigorous for longer." Professor Jim Fries, Stanford University (commenting upon results of his research at Stanford on aging exercisers).

- "Inactivity was once thought to prevent arthritis and protect fragile arthritic joints from further damage. More recent research has demonstrated the opposite." Benjamin Ebert, MD, PH.D., as quoted on Dr. Larry Smith's website.

Older runners reported pain and disability only 25% as often as those who didn't run. A study conduced by Fries, et al, Stanford group among runners over 50 who had been running for more than 20 years.

"Running or jogging does not increase the risk of osteoarthritis even though traditionally we thought it was a disease of wear and tear." Dr. Fries, from his study

"Reasonably long-duration, high mileage running need not be associated with premature degenerative joint disease of the lower extremities." Panush, et al, "Is Running Associated with Degenerative Joint Disease?" JAMA 1986. Subjects were at least 50 years old, average number of years running: 12; average weekly mileage: 28.

No increase in degenerative joint disease in runners. "Competitive sports increase joint risk — but running risk is low." Lane, et al, "Risk of Osteoarthritis (OA) with Running and Aging: Five Year Longitudinal Study." Studied runners 50-72 years old. Findings were similar to the conclusions of a study in 1989.

"Running seems to be devoid of adverse effects leading to knee degeneration, compared with other sports." Kujala, et al, "Knee Osteoarthritis in Former Runners, Soccer Players, Weight Lifters, and Shooters," (Arthritis & Rheumatism, 1995)

"Runners averaging 66 years of age have not experienced accelerated development of radiographic OA (Osteo-Arthritis) of the knee compared with nonrunner controls" Lane et al, Journal of Rheumatology 1998.

"Older individuals with OA of the knees (not end-stage) benefit from exercise." Ettinger, et al, JAMA 1997.

"Little or no risk of OA with lifelong distance running." Konradsen, et al, (AJSM 1990) studied a group that tends to abuse the orthopedic limits (former competitive runners) who ran 20-40 km per week for 40 years. Other interesting studies include Lane, et al, JAMA 1989, Kujala, et al, Arthritis & Rheumatism 1995.

For more areas of information on this topic, see *Running Until You're 100*, at www.jeffgalloway.com.

© Wojciech Gajda/iStockphoto/Thinkstock

53 I want to run faster

Our egos thrive on faster times. With each improvement, there is a temporary boost to the ego, often followed by motivation to train harder for even faster times. The ego thrives on improvement.

Caution: Don't let the time goal be your primary satisfaction from running. Enjoy the endorphins, the accomplishment in completing each workout, and the joy of learning new things about running. Most of the world-class runners with whom I've talked about this issue have enjoyed the journey to the top more than the recognition and performances on the elite stage.

To get faster, you must run faster during some targeted workouts. The plans in the books listed below will help you develop a coordinated strategy for improvement. While there are ego frustrations along the track to faster times, you'll learn some new things about yourself – usually more from the setbacks than the successes.

The speed workouts can improve your performance in many areas: muscle capacity, heart function, oxygen delivery, running mechanics, and the coordination of body parts and organs to keep going fast while tired.

The mental benefits may be more significant. As you tap into these enhancements, you will see yourself as one who can push on when tired and uncertain, and that you can rise up from a setback and improve. On some occasions, the attitude boost from faster runs is more powerful. As you become more capable in pushing back the physical barriers, you can receive more confidence and empowerment in your mental outlook on running and life.

Any form of speed training increases risk of injury. But if you follow the guidelines in the sidebar below, you can reduce this enhanced risk. There are also mental "injuries" that occur when you don't manage the stress or ego. Part of the speed training process is learning how to prevent these from occurring.

Mental training can be done while you are doing speedwork. Setting up and focusing on the strategic workouts puts you in the frontal lobe. This can maintain control over the reflex brain, managing and reducing the negative attitude hormones normally produced due to stress. The three cognitive training techniques in my *Mental Training* book could be applied during the workouts.

Set up your speed program and enjoy the faster times as you enjoy the good times spent running.

How to run faster

1. Set up a plan. You will find all of the elements needed for improvement in my books: *5K/10K, Half Marathon, Year Round Plan, Boston – How to Qualify,* and *Galloway Training Programs.*

2. Increase the distance of the long run beyond the race distance. Run the long runs slowly and follow the directions on page 144 to improve endurance.

3. Improve your running efficiency by doing some simple drills, such as those listed on pages 80-83.

4. Set up a series of speed workouts, as noted in the books above.

5. Use the "magic mile" time trial to monitor progress, as noted on page 138.

6. Strive to find enjoyment in every workout – even the tough ones.

7. By using a training plan, you're setting up a cognitive strategy. This gets the frontal lobe involved so that you can train the reflex brain to deal with stress and keep going.

54 I want to beat my obnoxious, bragging neighbor

In most running groups, there are usually a few runners whose aspirations exceed their accomplishments. Only a tiny percentage of these let their egos get the best of them and make unrealistic predictions and other claims. This makes them targets for other runners who want to show that talking doesn't get the muscles, heart, and mind ready for a goal.

Most commonly the bragger targets a key community race and tells everyone how well he or she is going to run. This allows one to out-train the bragger, which usually isn't hard to do. In my experience, these folks derive their satisfaction from impressing less-experienced runners with claims. Most that I've tracked don't have an adequate scheduled training program to achieve what they project and bounce from one type of training to the next based upon the most recent popular article in the media.

There is great satisfaction in setting up a plan and staying with it to the end. Whether you beat your neighbor or not, you will learn a lot about how to train and how to race. You'll discover some interesting things about yourself and how to push into challenges.

If all goes well, you will pass the neighbor during the last third of the race. Be sure to say "you're doing great." You don't have to say, "I'm sorry that this race didn't turn out the way you told us it would."

After the race, you will have the option of listening to the excuses of your neighbor or simply enjoying your accomplishment in following and fulfilling a plan.

Race day strategy

- Try to find your competitor and line up nearby at the start
- Avoid going out too fast, but keep the person in sight
- At the half-way point, start moving up
- With a mile to go, move behind the person and save some resources for your final push
- With half a mile to go, move past with strength, build up a lead
- Focus on the people ahead of you, not the people behind
- Your run-walk-run timer can be a psychological tool — your rival will hear you getting closer
- Most of the people you pass in the last half mile will not challenge you

Chapter 6
I run because
I am inspired

55 I am inspired by Billy Mills

The person who inspired me most grew up on the Pine Ridge Native American Reservation in South Dakota. Billy was selected to attend a boarding school where he discovered that he could run faster than other boys in the distance events. Realizing that this could be his path to success in life, he worked very hard and won a scholarship to the University of Kansas.

Billy has a positive sprit and envisioned himself becoming one of the best distance runners in the NCAA. This did not happen. He came to believe that his best events were longer ones and set his sights on the 10,000 meter. His coach, however, wanted him to run shorter events, and lots of them. The training prescribed on the university team did not prepare him for his 10K event, and he did not achieve what he thought was possible during his four years in Lawrence, KS.

© Ryan McVay/Digital Vision/Thinkstock

Post graduate running programs were few in 1961, but Billy found one: The U.S. Marines. After his officer training, he was assigned to the team at Quantico, VA, setting his sights on the Olympic 10K. His times were not yet good enough to qualify for the U.S. Olympic Trials, but he felt strongly that he would improve and qualify. Progress was slow.

A college running friend of Billy's returned to his native country after graduation (Australia) and trained with the 10K world record holder at the time, Ron Clark. Every week for about three years, Billy would get his "intelligence report" detailing Clark's workouts. Billy tried them and was usually unsuccessful. But at the end of the hard portion of his workout, Mills envisioned that Clark was just ahead of him, so he shifted into his best finish "kick" and imagined himself zooming by the world record holder, breaking the tape and becoming the Olympic champion. Almost every day for three years, this fantasy world was enacted.

In 1963, I went to watch the National Cross Country championships in New York City with some college friends. At the meet, I looked up an alumnus of my school, Wesleyan University, who was Officer in Charge of the Marine Team. When he discovered that I might be interested in applying in a few years and that I was interested in the 10K, he introduced me to Billy.

I instantly liked Billy. I didn't understand it at the time, but there was something about his attitude that impressed me. Later I came to understand that he had a subtle confidence that I had not encountered before. Mills was probably ranked about 25th going into that race. Without bragging, he told me that he was going to finish near the top. He did.

I followed Billy in *Track & Field News* as he continued to improve, qualified for the Olympic Trials and then, unexpectedly, made the team in the 10K and the Marathon. That experience made a major imprint on me. If Billy could come out of obscurity and make the Olympic team, maybe there was hope for me.

Billy Mills was not our best 10K runner (Lindgren) and was not ranked very high among the entrants in the 1964 Tokyo Olympic 10K. But somehow, he sensed that he had a chance to win. There was no trial heat, only a final with over 60 athletes running 25 times around the track.

The excitement and focus drove Mills to push the pace and at halfway he realized that he had run only one second slower than his fastest 5K. He was feeling the overexertion and feared that he had spent his resources. He looked for a place to drop out. Just before he stepped off the track, he glanced into the stands and happened to focus on one person: his wife, Pat.

He couldn't drop out with her watching, believing in his dream, so he decided to just finish the race. This released the pressure to win. Several runners passed him and then a group of about four runners went by. Something intuitively told Billy that he should go with that group and he did. Ron Clark was one of those runners.

Billy admits that he doesn't remember very much about the last four laps. He was exhausted and running on instinct, trying to put one foot in front of the other. The group passed one runner after another, and as they approached the "bell lap" (one to go), Billy was in lane 2, with Ron Clark in lane 1. They were approaching a slower runner who was a full lap behind, and Clark tapped Billy's arm, trying to get him to move out so that both could pass the runner. Billy was so "out of it" that he didn't know he was being nudged. So Clark finally shoved Billy out into the 4th lane and passed the runner.

The third member of the group, Mohammed Gamudi from Tunisia, was right behind, saw the altercation and took off after Clark. His arms were swinging erratically as he passed Mills and the sharp part of his elbow hit Billy very hard in his upper arm, hitting a nerve. The pain was great enough to wake Billy up and the reflex brain sent a primitive message from his playground days: When someone whomps you, you whomp them back. But his slow-twitch endurance muscle cells were spent and he could not respond. The front two runners moved away from Billy, and were about 30 meters ahead as Billy rounded the curve and looked at the finish only 100 meters away.

Billy was living the situation that he had rehearsed almost every day for three years. Without thinking, he did what he had programmed himself to do. And because he had practiced sprinting at the end of his hard workouts, he had trained his fast twitch muscle fibers to respond.

Mills zoomed by Gamudi and Clark, broke the tape and became the Olympic champion. This is the greatest upset, come-from-behind victory in the history of the Olympic 10K.

56 I am inspired by Lee Kilpack: Racing cancer

In 1996, Lee Kilpack was diagnosed with breast cancer, with lymph node involvement. She began a treatment plan of surgery, chemo, and radiation. Lee had never exercised. The diagnosis was a shock to her spirit, and the treatment tested her body, mind, and willpower.

By 2000, things weren't looking too good, and she felt bad most of the time. Then, one morning she woke up with the desire to start taking care of her body. She hired a personal trainer that day. By 2001, she was walking every day. Later that year, she had inserted some running into the walks. In 2002, Lee walked the 3-day, 60-mile Breast Cancer Walk and raised $3,000 for the cause.

> "If I had to choose between my old pre-cancer life as a somewhat depressed, overweight, unmotivated and unfulfilled couch potato and my current life with cancer, it's easy. I'm energetic, happy, motivated, and love life each day."
>
> *Lee Kilpack*

The training for and the completion of such a strenuous event resulted in a big letdown in motivation, with extended recovery from injuries, aches and pains. Lee struggled and finally started running regularly in December of 2003. After the '04 New Year, Lee set a bigger goal – to finish a marathon in November. The training program she chose was too adverse and she became injured in September. She didn't give up.

In early 2005, Lee's doctor cleared her to start running again. She picked up my conservative training program after attending my Blue Mountain beach retreat. I worked with her via email and often found it hard to hold back her energy and drive.

The training for the Marine Corps Marathon was more of a challenge than most because she relocated to the Gulf coast to volunteer for relief efforts after Hurricane Katrina – squeezing in runs after exhausting days. Somehow, she also hikes, cycles, and paddles hard in her kayak; on the "off days," she doesn't run. She finished with strength.

She regularly gets screened for tumor markers. While the tests show her out of the normal range, her doctor does not see a threat in the near future and supports her running.

"I don't know what the future holds for me. If it is metastasis tomorrow, I would be OK with that. What a good life I've been given. My health and happiness have never been better. What my oncologist doesn't understand is what a dynamite combo vitality and endorphins make."

57 I am inspired by Mavis Lindgren: Marathon records after age 80

Mavis Lindgren was a sickly child and sickly adult who was advised against exercising. She almost died of a lung infection in her late 50s. During the recovery, her new, young doctor had the shocking opinion that she should walk with her husband and kept recommending an increase in the distance she covered.

Surprisingly, Mavis found enjoyment as she felt her body come alive with improved endurance. In her 60s, she took up running with husband Carl and quickly surpassed him. Into her late 80s, she was setting age group records and had not even suffered a common cold since beginning her running career.

At about the age of 85, she slipped on a cup at the 20-mile water station at the Portland, OR, marathon. Officials helped her up and tried to take her to a medical tent. She quietly brushed them off, saying that it was a surface injury. After she finished, however, she went to the medical tent to find that she had been running with a broken arm.

© Pixland/Thinkstock

58 I am inspired by Dave Wottle: Don't give up

Because he was very thin and feeble, the Wottle family doctor recommended that Dave exercise and suggested running. Dave felt at home on the track team. Like many distance and middle distance runners, however, he had to work hard to see modest improvements in junior high and high school track. At Bowling Green State University, he improved significantly every year, and Dave moved to the top of the NCAA rankings. He was at his performance peak during the 1972 U.S. Olympic trials.

While the commentators were expecting running legend Jim Ryun to win the U.S. trials 1500 meters, Dave won easily. He also had no problem winning the 800 meter. During a workout the week after the trials, Dave injured his knee. Three weeks later, when we reported for our Olympic tour, Dave was still injured and had not been able to train.

The coaches wanted to send him home and bring in a healthy runner. Dave refused. Reluctantly, the coaches supported Wottle. By working with the athletic trainers and the medical team, he was able to run, and he gradually regained some conditioning.

After the gun fired on his first 800 meter heat in Munich, Dave was at the back of the pack. He struggled to move up as he rounded the final turn, passing one runner, then another. At the finish, he leaned, and finished third – the last qualifier for the next round.

Due to conditioning issues, Dave ran a similar race in the next two qualifying heats, coming from behind to barely qualify for the finals.

In the final, the competitors clumped together, going for the gold. Unfortunately, Dave could not keep up and had fallen about 30 yards behind at the halfway mark. Many competitors would have stepped off the track. But Dave set his sights on the next-to-last competitor and caught up with him as they rounded the final curve.

Two runners bumped one another and Dave darted between them. He ran inside to pass three more and outside to pass another group. As he approached the finish, there was a line of the leaders ahead, and at the last minute a parting occurred – Dave dove through, broke the tape, and won the Gold medal.

TV announcers were amazed at his finish spurt, but this was not the case. His 200 meter splits were almost identical. Dave knew what he could do and stuck with his plan.

At any given point, logic showed that Dave Wottle should have given up his spot and let someone else run. Dave won because he did not give up.

59 I am inspired by Lasse Viren:
When you get knocked down, get up

During the Munich Olympics, the star performer in my event, the 10,000 was not well known going into the games. Unlike most athletes who move onto the world class scene over a 4-8 year period, Lasse's times were not spectacular. When I checked on his performances the year before the Olympics, I noted that he had finished 17th in the European Championships 10K.

Lasse's joy was running through the wilds, mile after mile. He loved forest trails and had a variety of routes and workouts. About the only time that you saw Viren on a track was during a race. But as Lasse ran his trails, he would envision being in the big race, responding to various challenges and coming back strong. In the trial heat of the 10,000 Lasse ran a smart race and qualified easily without seeming to be very tired. None of the experts I spoke with before the 10K final predicted that he would finish in the top 5.

The 10K final evolved into a strategic race. With about 8 laps to go (out of 25), there were 10 runners tightly bunched, all in position to win the race. With no

warning, Lasse was tripped by a runner and he fell into the infield of the track, rolling over.

The first action that impressed me was that Viren ran straight back to where he had been tripped. If he had tried to run the tangent he would have taken too many steps on the infield and been disqualified. There was no doubt in my mind that he had rehearsed this possibility.

The second impressive act was not trying to catch up with the field in the first lap or two. Lasse gradually caught up with the pack over the next 2 laps, but he didn't stop there. During the following two laps, he passed one runner at a time.

With two laps to go, Viren moved into the lead and continued pick up the pace every 20 yards or so. There were several runners near him with half a lap to go, but Lasse steadily moved away from them. He not only won the Gold, but he set a world record.

Viren won the 5K gold medal in Munich and returned to Montreal four years later to capture gold in the 5K & 10K and finish 5th in the marathon.

Chapter 7
I want to be a role model/help others

60 To be an example to my children

Children tend to learn from observing adults and often follow parents' behavior patterns. Yes, they "do as we do" more than they "do as we say." Kids are observing us constantly and embedding in their subconscious brains the behaviors they see. These early childhood behavior patterns become hardwired to our reflex brain that initiates most of our actions.

While this information is somewhat scary, there is a positive side. While we need to be aware of avoiding negative behaviors, we can influence kids to engage in positive ones by doing them. Studies show that parents who regularly exercise tend to have children who exercise.

© Jupiterimages/Goodshoot/Thinkstock

But the kids are learning by your actions. If you complain about having to do your run or whine about how tough the run is, they will learn that running hurts and is something you have to take like medicine.

But if you talk about and demonstrate a good attitude after running, they are likely to do the same. If you explain how running enhances your thinking, attitude, and life, they are more likely to follow in your running steps. Even when children are young, you can still talk positively about exercise and make a big impression.

In my book *Fit Kids — Smarter Kids*, there is more information about the benefits kids receive from exercise at all ages and how to exercise together. But if you travel a lot and can't run in person, send emails, text messages, or explain how you are getting in your runs on a busy trip and how good you feel because you're doing this. Also encourage them to tell you about their exercise as they tell you about their day.

Thousands of adults have told me that because their Mom ran from the time they could remember, they assumed that running is what adults do. When they reached a certain age, they ran, too.

How to be a good exercise role model

- Talk about how good you feel after a run
- Explain how running activates the brain and makes you smart
- Tell the child "you can enjoy these benefits also"
- Say "you are a runner" regularly

61 To exercise with my children/grandchildren

One of the great joys for parents is to exercise with their kids. There is a special bonding that occurs when this happens. Even when children don't look forward to the workout, follow the guidelines below and get out there with them. It's possible to have some fun in every run. It's also OK to offer rewards afterward.

© Monkey Business Images Ltd/Valueline/Thinkstock

Fit kids are smarter kids. As I researched the book with that title, I discovered hundreds of studies that document the proof. Children who regularly exercise do better in school and better in life. The earlier children start to enjoy uplifting run-walks, the more likely they will become life-long exercisers.

Experts believe that when kids (and adults) exercise aerobically, the frontal lobe is stimulated. This is the executive brain that designs strategy, makes decisions, and gains control over the situation. Aerobic endurance activity has been shown to stimulate new brain cell growth.

By arranging the amount of walking and running, you can share a run with your family members. If you hear any huffing and puffing, back off the pace and insert more walking.

Set aside a time each week for "family fitness." Make it a point to get everyone out there for this fun exercise. If kids are too tied to their TV/texting/computer, let them earn time by exercising.

You will treasure the time you spend running and walking with your kids. If you make it fun, they will too.

62 To help a friend get into running

One of the very best ways to consolidate the items you've learned from exercise is to help someone get started. Not only will you realize how much you have learned, but you'll see the "big picture" better as you explain the benefits of exercise to a novice. Almost certainly, you'll enjoy running even more.

The best part of this experience is the inner satisfaction. You're not only helping someone, you're also introducing him to an activity that can improve the quality of his life – for the rest of his life.
Running with a friend can improve motivation for both of you. There is a special chemistry in the relationship between someone who is trying to improve health and the quality of life and the person who wants to make the change. Many lifelong friendships are forged during this experience.

Mentors experience a revival in motivation as they stay in touch with the student. As problems are solved, the teacher will often reconnect with the life-enhancing benefits of running, realizing that she had been taking them for granted. On the low motivation day, the more experienced runner will realize during the pep talk that she's receiving as much from the talk as the novice.

As you explain the benefits of running and the reasons behind the various training elements, you'll probably learn (or remind yourself of) a number of new things that enrich your own experience. One of the best rewards is to see new runners thrive as they progress.

Running on the more scenic trails gives you an excuse to enjoy running areas you don't normally visit. These runs are "special treats" that we all need but often don't do. Mentoring gives you a chance to attend events you like and run with fun groups you haven't run with for a while.

So call up a friend and help yourself to more enjoyable runs.

Being a good coach

Get them a good textbook – *Getting Started* has a 6-month entry-level program, as does *A Woman's Guide to Fat-Burning*. Other good books are *Running Until You're 100* and *5K/10K*.

Go over a chapter at a time, starting at the beginning. Highlight the key passages in the book for him or her. You don't have to do this with every chapter, but it really helps to get a novice headed in the right direction.

Make each session enjoyable – especially during the first month

If your mentee is huffing and puffing, slow down and walk more from the beginning of every session. If there is a continuing challenge, then stop for that day. There shouldn't be any huffing and puffing for several months, if then.

Find interesting areas where you can run – scenic areas, smooth trails

Convenient running and walking routes near work or home are best for busy people most of the time. But once a week, an excursion to an interesting area can be very rewarding. It's great to have variety, and you should give your mentee some choice.

On each run, have a joke, a juicy story, and/or maybe a controversial issue

This will break the ice, inject some humor, and help to make for a positive bonding experience. With beginners who are having a hard time getting into it, the little humorous items are often appreciated as much as the shoes and clothing.

Don't push too hard, but encourage

One of the most difficult decisions in coaching is whether to push or back off – whether to use a pat on the back or a kick in the butt. In general, it is important that the person gets out there and exercises regularly with some enjoyment from each session. When motivation is down, just shoot for a minimal amount every other day. Realize, however, that to really get hooked, the new runner must develop the desire from within.

Rewards work!

After a certain number of weeks, or after reaching a certain level of fitness, surprise your mentee with a reward. It doesn't have to be something expensive or exotic. The reward allows the new exerciser to focus on his or her progress, and feel the satisfaction of steady work paying off. Your positive comments are the most powerful reward for a beginner.

When your mentee is ready, find a fun race to attend

Races are such positive experiences for new runners when they have a good leader to coach them through the experience: calming the anxieties and sharing the celebration. Your new exerciser will almost always realize that he or she is like most of the others in the race. Just having a race date on a calendar will provide the beginner with an identity that will increase motivation.

Your greatest reward will be an independent exerciser

Take it as a real compliment that your mentee will need less and less of your guidance. This means that you were an excellent coach, and that he or she can coach a new runner and enrich another life – and you can too.

63 Run for a cause

When you're helping others who need help, you tap into an enhanced motivational boost. Our Galloway training program provides the training support for several charities that raise funds through events. Most runners have a special connection with the charity.

Most charities ask for a certain amount as a donation for that season. Those who complete the fundraising are rewarded with a trip to a marathon. In many cases, the marathon enrollment has been filled so the runner gets into a prized event.

Making the pledge gets you committed to the goal. You believe in the cause, they need your help, and you must follow through with the promise. Some charities will match you up with a patient. As you get to know that person, you have a direct connection to the cause and become part of the community.

Helping others. There is a boost to the immune system when you help others. When you really believe that you are helping others, there's an additional boost. If you were just running for yourself, there are a number of days when you will roll over in bed. As you think about the people that are counting on you to achieve your goal, you receive an extra boost.

Teamwork in fundraising. Charity support means raising funds as your training increases. You quickly meet others on your team who will give you help and support. Most charities will connect you with two energetic teams – your running team and your fund raising team — to increase motivation further.

The event weekend brings it all together. Sharing experiences with team members and then running together is often a peak experience. Crossing the finish line symbolizes bringing together the physical improvements, the fundraising and the helping of others at the same time.

How to find a charity

- If you have a favorite charity or cause, ask the office personnel if they offer a marathon or half marathon fundraising program

- Pick a charity category and Google it, searching for "marathon fundraising"

- If there is a particular event you want to run, but the registration is closed, go to the website and click on some of the charity groups to see if they have any slots left

- Want to end breast cancer? Try www.breastcancermarathon.com.

- Want to run in the "original" Athens Marathon? Try www.athensmarathon.com. Ask about the AHEPA program.

© Hemera/Thinkstock

64 Run to end breast cancer

www.breastcancermarathon.com

Usually held in mid February, the 26.2 with Donna contains a half and a full marathon. Put the date of this race on your calendar and you're certain to get an extra series of motivation boosts. When you see women who are currently going through chemo and/or radiation running a half marathon, it's hard to say you aren't going to run because it's raining outside, etc. The Marathon to Finish Breast Cancer (26.2 with Donna) is uplifting, fun, and motivating, in addition to including run-walk-run pace groups.

There are a lot of big events that try to help charities. I don't know of any large event that has given virtually penny of the entry fee to breast cancer research and care for women with the disease except for this event.

Donna Deegan is an on-air news personality in the Jacksonville area who has fought off breast cancer three times. She believes that the only way to rid the planet of this disease is to raise funds for quality research. Millions have been raised for productive research done by the Mayo Clinic, where the race starts and finishes.

The course runs parallel to Jacksonville Beach, Atlantic Beach, and Neptune Beach, with frequent vistas of the ocean and the intercoastal waterway. One

segment is on the hard-packed beach itself. Each beach community turns out to cheer you with their own version of "cheer parties."

You feel so good. You not only finish a marathon or half, but so many of the spectators turn out because of their connection with breast cancer and thank you. Some are running in honor of a mom or sister. It's hard not to get emotional when a little girl holds up a sign saying "You're running this for my mom."

Our Galloway Training Program leaders organize the pace groups. That means that each group uses the appropriate run-walk-run strategy based upon the pace per mile. You are supported throughout.

I hope to see you there!

The marathon to finish breast cancer

Where: Jacksonville, FL

When: Usually mid February

Website: www.breastcancermarathon.com

Why: To raise funds for research and to help women with breast cancer

Do you have to make a donation? No, you help by entering the race; no fundraising is required.

© Fernando Alonso Herrera/iStockphoto/Thinkstock

Chapter 8
To spend quality time with friends

65 I enjoy the social time with my running group

Thousands of runners have told me that they would only run about half of their current running days per year it weren't for the motivation boost they get from their running group.

Because the group is there even once a week, it's easier to get out of bed early. You feel the energy of the group members as you contemplate rolling over in bed. You know that if you don't join them, you will have to answer their emails or explain your laziness in person when you see them. As you get ready, you will feel the group support and look forward to it.

If the afternoon is the best time for you to run, try to find an after-work running group. Because the group is waiting, one tends to run in the afternoons even after a long and stressful day. There's an obligation to get together and, once running, a chemistry that erases the end-of-the-day fatigue.

Because of the group, there's more support to finish the tough workouts. When in the right group, the power of the community is greater than the sum of the individuals. While running with one or more teammates, unexpected strength emerges to push through adversity. An additional wave of positive energy is bestowed as you give support to others who need it.

Because of the group, I have the best friendships. The bonding that occurs in running groups is personal, honest, and empowering. Life-long friendships have been made in practically every running group with which I've been associated.

Most group members feel supported even on the solo runs between group runs. During the week, when running on my own, I don't want to let my group down by getting out of shape. As I struggle to get out of bed or out the door after work, I think of the other group members overcoming their motivation issues and running. I feel empowered through this connection.

Group running guidelines

Having organized Galloway training groups for about 40 years, I have found that these are the factors that tend to lead to fun and bonding, improving motivation for all members.

1. Choose the right group. Make sure that the group pace is not too fast for you. By using a simple "magic mile" time trial (see Year Round Plan and/or other training books), you can compute your current potential and set a safe pace for long runs – two min/mi slower than your current predicted all-out marathon pace.

2. On long runs, make sure that someone stays with the slowest member. It's common for one group member to have a bad day. The group leader should designate a person to be the support backup and stay with anyone who needs support.

3. Set up rules for water breaks. Some groups spend too much time around the water cooler. The general principle is simple: fill up your cup, move aside for the next person to fill up, and drink the water as you walk.

4. Set up rules for walk breaks. The group leader should designate the run-walk-run strategy for that day at the beginning of the run. The pace of the slowest member of the group should dictate pace and run-walk-run strategy. You cannot go too slow on long runs.

5. Secrets are divulged during runs. Remember: what is said in the group, stays with the group.

Note: To find out more about Galloway Training Groups, visit www.jeffgalloway.com

© Hemera/Thinkstock

66 Running helps to "talk things out"

When runners talk during a run, they tend to be more honest and guttural. Some of my most interesting and open conversations have occurred during a run. This is probably due to some hardwired instincts going back millions of years.

Trust during long treks. According to anthropologists who study ancient man, our ancient ancestors first developed the "human" social behavior patterns when they migrated together during Paleolithic times. Those who cooperated had a better chance of survival by supporting one another.

When we run, the "human brain" is activated. This is the center for conscious thought, where language and speech are controlled. It's very common to see a normally shy person change into a talker during a run with friends. There is a sense of intuitive trust that allows running group members to speak honestly.

Parents who run with their kids often discover information and feelings they would never find in other family experiences. Friends can reconnect during a run and bring each other up to date after two decades often during one run.

When there is a tough issue between individuals, a walk or run can promote relaxation, a lowering of anxiety, and honest communication.

So there are often statements made in confidence during a run. Remember the runner's rule of trust: what is said on a run, stays on the run.

67 Challenge a friend to a race

A significant number of the new runners today got off the couch because they responded to a challenge. One friend challenges a friend to complete an event such as the Epcot Wine & Dine Half Marathon at Disney World. In many cases, one or both have not been doing any training. Both friends find that they have more fun as they get to know one another better.

One + one = motivation. Even when living in different cities, the connection through training can enrich a relationship while giving each person a motivation boost. There's a special personal chemistry that occurs when one person wants to help another get in better shape.

Meaningful connection. The novice wants to realize the expectations of the mentor and usually asks one question after another. The mentor realizes the need to offer good advice and will read books such as *Galloway's Marathon FAQs* or *Half Marathon*. The books have actually been great ways to fill the information gaps and proceed in a coordinated way.

Reward Race weekend. The planning for race weekend offers another bonding experience: registering for the race, travel, hotel, sightseeing in the area, etc. The first longer race experience is a big deal and should be savored as much as possible.

Empowering accomplishment: In almost every case, the challenges are met and the weekend is a very memorable event. But the power of the experience was in the communication among friends for months leading up to the race day. This will be remembered by both runners for the rest of their lives.

Race Challenges

- Big city races: NYC, Chicago, Marine Corps Marathon (DC) Note: due to lottery registration, make sure that both runners are accepted.

- Interesting city races: Alaska Wild Marathon, Missoula Marathon, and Portland, OR

- Beautiful Courses: Big Sur, Ogden, Space Coast

- Where all family members can enjoy the run: RunDisney events (www. runDisney.com)

- Memorable: Athens Marathon (www.athensmarathon.com), Rome Marathon (www.runitaly.com)

- For the cause: The Marathon to Finish Breast Cancer (Jacksonville, FL)

68 The special bond that occurs during a run

I meet a lot of people during the year, and I try to recognize something to respect in each one. Try as I might, I don't usually have the memory to pull up all of this when I see the person again at another clinic, expo, or consultation at my Phidippides store in Atlanta.

But when another runner reminds me of a certain run, something about the course, the weather, or the events of the day, I usually remember not only the run, but I feel a sense of the personalities of the other runners on that run.

There is a special chemistry that brings two or more people together during a run. Many have described this as "psychic energy" that is transmitted and received in areas of the brain that we don't use as much as we did in ancient times.

Some anthropologists believe that the human traits of cooperation, teamwork, caring, and supporting one another were developed during a million-year period. Our Paleolithic ancestors went from being fiercely individualistic to begrudging companions for protection. With the evolution of tribes, our ancestors learned to rely upon one another and, at some point, care for and respect one another.

We are molded by our behaviors. Our Paleolithic relatives were moving constantly every day in the search of food and shelter. Forward motion exercise (walking/running) literally brought our ancient ancestors together. Gradually, they developed the intuitive communication that we have inherited and enjoy during a run.

The best communication occurs when stress is low. Running and walking at a gentle pace trigger a release of the stress of life and positive attitude hormones.

We will tend to be more upbeat and open to talking and sharing when the pace is gentle and easy. As the effort level rises, so does the stress level. At a certain stress level, the exercise is too hard and communication stops.

Sometimes running at a fast pace will result in bonding of a different type. When runners are trying to achieve a time goal that is challenging, speed training becomes very important. Having one or more partners to pull you along will usually result in fewer workout dropouts, better quality, and better performances at the end. Going thought a training season together brings people together.

When you share a run with a stranger, be prepared to have a new friend by the time you have finished.

69 Run with a friend or spouse who is slower

Running more slowly, even several minutes per mile slower than you usually run on an easy day, will not result in a loss of fitness. This allows you to share special time with a spouse, a new runner, or an old running friend who is returning to running after some time off.

Running slower may help you. If you have a tendency to run too fast on easy days or are not slowing down enough on long runs, your slower running buddy can allow you to recover from your long or faster workouts and avoid overuse injuries.

If you're having trouble slowing down, take walk breaks more frequently. Many men tell me that they cannot run slow enough to run with their wives. This can be true when running continuously. By using frequent walk breaks, most couples can find a ratio that works. For example, if it's hard to slow down to 10 min/mile by running for 3 minutes/walking for one minute, then try 2/1 or 60 seconds running/30 seconds walking. Some couples can run 10 to 11 min/mi by running 1/1.

The slower runner can use the run as a speed workout. In this case, the faster runner won't have to slow down as much, but the faster runner needs to monitor pace and ensure that this is not excessive for the running buddy.

So run with a buddy on one of your slow days and help him or her improve speed.

70 Run with a friend who is faster

If you run slowly all the time, you probably won't run any faster. But by running with a faster friend, you can pick up your pace without doing injury-risking speedwork.

Talk with a friend who will help you. You want someone who can gently pace you slightly faster than you have been currently running. Some runners don't have a good sense of pace and will run much too fast. You will either need to have a GPS device to measure pace or run on a marked and measured course.

Discuss pace in detail. You should run the first 5 minutes as a slow warm-up. Then run 5 minutes at your normal easy running pace. Pick it up for the next 5 minutes to the pace you would run on a fast day. Then talk with your friend about how you want to run the rest of the workout. In general, it's best to run 5-10 minutes at your target faster pace and then slow down for 3-5 minutes at a slower pace to recover.

Discuss walk break frequency. It may surprise you, but walk breaks usually allow runners to run faster than when running continuously. You can use the run-walk-run guidelines on page 50.

During the workout, if the pace is just too fast for you on that day, tell your friend. It helps no one to push beyond current limits.

Rest the day before this workout. You want to come into the run with fresh legs. Have fun!

71 A long-running friendship

The best friendships that I have, that have lasted over the longest period, were forged by running. I stay in touch with some of the original group of kids (at the time) I tried to stay with over 50 years ago on my first runs at Westminster Schools. When I share a series of runs with someone, I almost always like them and treasure the association of new friendship. That's how things started when I met Geoff Hollister.

Geoff and I literally ran into one another in Newport, RI, in 1966. We were attending Officer Candidate School for the US Navy. At the end of the week was a relay. There weren't many of the OC's who ran competitively so during the first two weeks, I had no competition passing runners and winning the race. The third race was different.

It was not unusual to receive the handoff with other runners and behind others. I grabbed the relay baton and quickly passed the runners around and ahead, except for one. During the second half of the race, I tried to move ahead and could not. He and I exchanged the lead several times and neither of us can remember who won.

We were instant friends. We had similar backgrounds, were liberal arts students, and liked to compete. But as we sent letters back and forth, we shared a passion for the joy of running and a growing sense that there was a culture developing around running. Wesleyan was within driving distance of the New England road racing circuit. My cross country teammates were Amby Burfoot (later, Boston marathon champion in 1968) and Bill Rodgers (later, 4-time winner of the Boston and New York marathons). Geoff was very much involved in the exciting track culture and jogging boom, which was developing in Eugene, OR, inspired by Geoff's mentor Bill Bowerman.

Geoff invited me to Eugene before I left for Vietnam in 1967. I spent 5 days running with him and his teammates on trails, the Oregon coast, and listening to Bowerman's wisdom.

Bill was in charge of the track/cross country program at the University of Oregon, but he had created an energized running community in his hometown of Eugene by producing some of the nation's top runners, particularly in the middle and long distances. Bowerman had observed a recreational jogging boom on a trip to New Zealand and had initiated adult beginning running classes out of the U of O campus. His book, *Jogging*, sold over a million copies in the mid 1960s.

Geoff told me about leading jogging groups (which used walk breaks) and the many innovative Bowerman projects: shoe design, faster tracks that reduced injuries, and a tiny new American sports shoe company called Blue Ribbon Sports (later, Nike). During a visit to Eugene, I helped Geoff open a BRS store in Eugene. This experience inspired me to open my store, Phidippides, in 1973 with Geoff's help as advisor and mentor.

A "walk on" 800 meter runner for the Ducks, Phil Knight, got an MBA in the early '60s and talked Bowerman into being his partner in Blue Ribbon Sports. Geoff signed on from the beginning, was listed as the #3 employee, and did lots of odd jobs including selling shoes out of the trunk of his car. I started doing the same in the Atlanta area and out of my dorm room in Connecticut.

Geoff graduated in 1968 and was assigned to the same type of ship in the same Vietnam area of operation. We had runs together to relieve the stress of not being able to run when at sea and other military issues. I returned from my three years of active duty and kept him informed about the excitement that was building in the South with my new team, the Florida Track Club.

Geoff returned from the Navy in 1971 just as BRS changed its name to Nike. He was expanding the company's presence in promotions while managing a company store in Eugene. He became a mentor to Steve Prefontaine. Pre told me on several occasions how Geoff taught him about business and life.

Many innovations and projects have been inspired or nurtured by Geoff. We have continued to work on various projects. He was involved in the movie *Prefontaine* and has produced several documentaries.

To this day, Geoff is my dearest friend, and we are in regular touch. During the past few years, he has battled cancer. The worst effect has been the loss of his running. He is constantly working on new projects and pursuing his other loves: wife Wendy, classic cars, sailing, and producing documentaries.

On July 12 of this year, Geoff's PET scan showed that the treatment was working and he was not threatened by the cancer. This was the best birthday present I have received.

72 Racing my friend/rival in a virtual race

There's nothing more motivating for some runners than challenging another runner to a race. Unfortunately, due to schedules, career, family, and other demands, the two "rivals" may not be able to get together in the same place at the same time.

Technology now allows runners to race one another when they live hundreds or thousands of miles apart. Various platforms (most commonly GPS) can track speed and distance and compare progress with others.

Because there is a date on the calendar and an opponent, runners tend to get in more of their scheduled training runs. On days when they tend to slack off, they imagine that their competitor is getting in a good workout. This tends to get lazy runners out the door.

Developing a strategy keeps one focused and under the control of the frontal lobe — as does analyzing the strengths and weaknesses of the opponent. This gives one more control over positive attitude hormones and can reduce the production of negative ones.

Comparing notes, arranging competition, setting up the ground rules all serve to bring the two runners together. Even before the big day, the bonding occurs.

Runners who have shied away from competitive experiences have embraced virtual racing. It offers fun on several levels.

Virtual racing guidelines

- Level course — or similar terrain
- Comparable weather — or adjustments
- Practice on the technology
- Set up rules between one another

73 To be with my friends – my training group

I get to run with dozens of different groups during my trips to Galloway Training Program kickoffs and Phidippides fun runs in Atlanta. Each time, a unique and powerful sense of bonding develops when we run together. Even when little or nothing has been said, the experience of sharing the challenge, feeling the exertion, finishing, and comparing notes brings runners closer.

You don't want to disappoint a friend by not showing up. Thousands of runners have told me that if they didn't have the scheduled run with their group, they wouldn't run half as much.

We weave our lives constantly with plots and sub-plots. During a run, the important and fun aspects emerge. A doctor, scientist, or teacher becomes a fellow runner and a real human being. The sharing of common experiences and problems brings us together. Runners support one another.

What is said on a run, stays on the run. Runners share aspects of their lives with fellow runners because of the trust.

My wife Barbara and I run together whenever we can. Currently, we run a marathon a month, side by side. Running brought us together and is a continuing strong thread in our relationship.

© Comstock/Thinkstock

Chapter 9
To explore

74 Exploring new cities

Upon my arrival in a new city, I can't wait to run and "discover" it. Embedded in the genetic circuits bestowed by our ancient ancestors is what I call "the exploration gene." Running allows us to cover more ground, smell more aromas, hear the accents or languages, touch the ground, and be affected by the colors, the architecture, the flora, and fauna. When there is unusual stimuli, the executive brain in the frontal lobe goes into high gear, using the logical (left) side and the intuitive (right side) to analyze the stimuli. It's fun to observe things that long-term residents weren't aware of.

As I give in to my territorial instinct, I want to move farther, block by block, scene by scene. I'm the explorer, pushing into new areas, bringing back the reports. All of this keeps me in the moment, in the conscious brain.

I'm fortunate to have a good sense of direction and enjoy using this instinct. It's sometimes a challenge to keep track of the turns and general direction, but I'm usually rewarded by finding my way back. When lost, it's not usually more than a few minutes and this allows for more exploring. Be sure to follow local safety guidelines and the navigation suggestions below.

The images received on the first run in a new location are often the most powerful memories of that city. So I try to stay in a district that offers good running and interesting things to see.

© diego cervo/iStockphoto/Thinkstock

If you are in the area for several days, explore other safe areas, take transit, or drive to interesting districts.

Let's move the legs and investigate!

75 Running in new places

- Contact running stores in the area in advance and ask for hotels near good running areas
- Contact running clubs in the area and ask for the best places to run
- Ask hotel staff for interesting and safe running routes
- Are there vistas, historical sites, or landmarks?
- Use a GPS device and mark your starting point
- As a backup, bring a cell phone with the hotel phone number
- Bring a map of the area you are running and mark the intersections as you run them.
- A simple way to avoid getting lost: run in one direction away from your hotel, don't make any turns, and turn around.

76 To explore my home "territory"

Territorial instincts have been passed on from our animal ancestors. Running through my neighborhood instantly connects me with these ancient roots and bestows a sense of belonging. I travel a lot and one of the joys of the return is that first run through on my favorite streets. I don't feel really "home" until I've run through my community. When staying at my Florida retreat, I have several venues: the pine trails, the beach, the bike trail.

The scenery is pleasant, sometimes breathtaking. But on each run I've learned to appreciate different aromas from trees or flowers, interesting patterns of sunlight through the trees, renovations or landscaping changes, or yard decorations. Each is a visual image that is processed in the brain's memory bank. The result is an ever-evolving puzzle based upon the impressions from my runs.

I've walked through the neighborhood and not received the same invigoration or effect. I believe that the activation of the conscious brain, which occurs during a run, can rev up the perception, the sorting, and the effect afterward. Again, running enhances what could be a boring tour through the same neighborhood.

Because runners can cover more ground, regularly, they tend to have a more expanded sense of their territory than average citizens. This pattern probably evolved from ancient patterns of running around and around the tribal camp to make sure everything was all right.

There are a number of interesting things to check on out there. Put on your shoes and cover your territory!

© Roberto Caucino/iStockphoto/Thinkstock

77 A destination race – history, scenic

Destination races are held in interesting geographical areas. Training for such an event is only one of the stimulating challenges. Selecting the right one and coordinating with family/friends makes it into a project. The strategy and planning required activate your frontal lobe. Once you look over the possibilities and get others involved, it's possible to find a location where everyone will win.

A growing number of runners are choosing one of the runDisney events as their goal. Family members who were neglected, at least a little, during your training can be rewarded with the trip. The anticipation and then the travel to a desirable location makes the training more motivating.

This allows you to demonstrate the concept of "delayed gratification." Many events, such as the runDisney series, have races for kids. You can train with

family members to prepare for the event. When all family members are preparing for an event and then going to a good place, team spirit improves.

If you have a non-running spouse or friend, pick a place that he or she would like to go. Arrange for sightseeing days before or after the event. Some activities might be playing golf, going to a pro sports game, or shopping at outlet malls while you are running.

Historical areas, such as Washington, DC, Boston, Williamsburg, etc., offer learning experiences for kids and adults. There are several marathons located near our national parks.

With the right run-walk-run strategy, one does not have to be "out of commission" after a half or full marathon. It is always gratifying to me to see thousands of medal-wearing runners the day after the Walt Disney World Marathon, Princess, Tinkerbell Half, Wine & Dine or Disneyland Half enjoying the park with their kids or spouse.

Destination events in the US

Near National Parks:

- St. George, UT: Bryce Canyon National Park (NP), Zion NP

- Missoula, MT: Glacier NP, Flathead Lake

- Billings, MT: Yellowstone NP, Grand Tetons NP

- Fresno, CA: Yosemite NP, Sequoia NP

Near Historical Areas:

- "The Original" www.athensmarathon.com

- Rome, Italy www.runitaly.com

- Chickamauga, GA/TN: Civil War battlefield

- Williamsburg, VA: Historical settlement, various battlefields

- Washington, DC

- Boston, MA

Scenic:

- Big Sur (Carmel/Monterey, CA)

- Ogden, UT

- Space Coast (Cocoa Beach, FL)

- Deadwood, SD

Entertainment/Fun:

- RunDisney series

Big City events: for the concerts, opera, cultural events

- NYC

- Marine Corps Marathon

- Chicago

Feel good/help a cause:

- Marathon to Finish Breast Cancer, Jacksonville, FL

78 The invigoration of running on a trail

I love running on trails that have a relatively smooth surface. I seem to get a "discount" on the fatigue: I'm only half as tired, even after running more distance than I usually run. There are several trails near our Tahoe running retreat location that have provided the best running I've experienced, and others at our Blue Mountain Beach retreat in Florida that I run regularly.

The natural environment allows you to be a part of nature. You're an animal moving through the forest, finding your way, smelling, feeling, and seeing the wonders of nature. Every few seconds, there is something interesting.

Get good advice before trying a new trail. Be sure to ask about the items on the "trail checklist" below. Many running stores or running clubs will have a local trail expert who can advise you. Don't be afraid to ask any question.

Those who are prone to ankle instability or other terrain issues may not be able to use certain trails. Most runners can avoid instability issues by walking carefully through rough trail segments. It helps to get good advice from a trail expert about the type of terrain to be expected.

TRAIL CHECKLIST

Ask an expert before selecting a trail. Ask about the safety of the area, the terrain, whether you are likely to encounter wild animals, etc. Be sure to identify the issues that have caused problems for other runners.

Run with a buddy. If one member of the duo is directionally challenged, the other should be a reasonably good pathfinder. If you're carrying items such as water or blood sugar boosting foods, coordinate who is bringing what. Have a planning session to prepare for the run and make up a checklist of the things you will need.

Bring a map of the trail area or draw one. Many parks have trail maps online and you can print them out. If you cannot get a printed copy, bring a paper and pencil with you and draw your own map of the route.

Bring a GPS/cell phone. The navigational devices have opened up trail running to many more runners. Be sure your batteries are charged.

Bring water. I like the ifitness water belt because it has 2-3 smaller bottles and stays snug around the waist.

Prepare for adverse weather. If cold, wear layers that can be tied around your waist. Look at the "clothing thermometer" in my books and www.jeffgalloway.com and adjust your apparel accordingly.

Be aware of the turns on the trail. Stop at each new intersection and see what the area looks like from the direction you will be approaching on the return. Mark it. Enjoy the experience.

79 Run through an interesting neighborhood

It motivates me to run through some of the older neighborhoods in my hometown of Atlanta and other cities I visit. It is interesting to see the different styles, the renovations, the landscaping.

© Catherine Yeulet/iStockphoto/Thinkstock

My first running store in Atlanta, Phidippides, is located near a treasure trove of these houses. I love noticing the different architectural periods represented, imagining what life was like during the various eras when they were built, etc.

Old parks are fascinating to me. There are several running loops from Phidippides into Piedmont Park, where the Peachtree road race finishes. This was originally conceived by Frederick Law Olmsted, the nation's foremost landscape architect, and constructed as the site for the Cotton States Exposition in 1895.

The bigger city parks, such as Piedmont Park, Central Park in New York, etc., allow for traffic-free running through various loops and environments. Before running in a park where you have not been before, be sure to find out if there are areas that are not especially safe.

Neighborhoods have their own personality. As you run, imagine what it would be like to live there, what the house would look like inside, and what historical events could have taken place there.

Seeing some of the designs has prompted many runners to read more about the history of the area. A common statement is "I ran by there 100 times and didn't have any idea what happened there."

80 Run a famous race course

When visiting Boston, NYC, Washington, DC, etc., consider running part of the famous marathons in those cities. Look at the event website for course information, get out a map, and plan your runs.

Some runners will choose a hotel on or near the race course. Be sure to check with the prospective hotel to ensure that the section of the course you want to run is safe. Check with local running clubs to find some of the more interesting sections of the course.

Schedule a run on part of the course. If you have to drive or take transportation to or from the running segment, you can add this to the projected running time. Bring maps, GPS device, cell phone.

Suggested course segments

Boston – You'll find a good course description, mile by mile, with comments by Bill Rodgers, in my book *Boston – How to Qualify*. Many like to stay downtown and run the last 2-3 miles of the course.

NYC – The NYC Marathon finishes in Central Park. This is a great place to run and you can imagine being in contention for the win as you approach the finish area near the Tavern on the Green.

DC – The Mall. I've run the Marine Corps Marathon many times, and my favorite segment is running "the mall." This is the green area from the Capitol to the Lincoln Memorial. If you want to stay on the flat, run up one side, cut in front of the Capitol and back on the other side, returning on one of the cross streets at the Washington Monument or the Lincoln Memorial. Add a hill (and about 1.5 miles) by making a circle up Capitol Hill and around the Capitol.

Jacksonville, Florida – The 26.2 with Donna Marathon to Finish Breast Cancer runs mostly parallel to Jacksonville Beach and the beach communities in that area.

Orlando – Disney World Marathon/EPCOT Wine & Dine Finish. There is a pleasant running/walking area that circles the lagoon at the Boardwalk area near the back gate to EPCOT with an extension running to the entrance of Hollywood Studios. There are several hotels right there: Beach Club, Yacht Club, Boardwalk, Swan and Dolphin.

81 Run the original marathon

No other sport has the authentic historical connection going back more than two and a half thousand years as does distance running. Running on the "original course" is only one of the great experiences. You can learn how distance running messengers were strands in the fabric of ancient Greece, how for the first 100 years of the Olympics there was only one event (a running race), and how the ancient Greeks used the Olympics to date historical events.

For about two decades, I have made an annual pilgrimage to Athens, Greece, for the annual running of the "original." On this Apostolos Tour, I've met many great people and most have told me how motivating it was to train for that event and run it.

You're running the route used by the ancient messenger (Phidippides was given credit for this). This is also the route used in the first marathon race in history in the 1896 Olympics. The 2004 Olympic Marathon used the same route. You'll finish in the spectacular stadium used in the first modern Olympic games in 1896.

Running is directly connected to the development of the democratic institutions we take for granted. The ancient Greeks were the first civilization to recognize excellence in fitness and athletic performance as an important goal in itself and established the ancient Olympic Games in 776 BC. So important were the games to the Greeks that they set historical dates based upon the most recent Olympiad.

The messengers were amazing. Not only did they have to be ready to run up to 150 miles at a moment's notice, but they delivered important news, negotiated business deals and treaties, acted as trusted diplomats, and then returned to the group that sent them with important information.

Past participants also tend to relate how motivating it is to tell other runners about their experiences. This often provides a 6-12 month motivation boost afterward. When you continue to run long distances and then relate your experiences, you're following in the footsteps of Phidippides. Tour the original marathon with Apostolos Greek Tours: www.athensmarathon.com

© Hemera/iStockphoto/Thinkstock

Chapter 10
To be all that I can be

82 To put myself to the test – time goal

Most citizens of the 21st century never know what it is like to push themselves to their physical limits. Training to finish the half or full marathon stimulates many couch sitters to dig deep for the motivation to meet regular challenges. The addition of a time goal that is challenging regularly requires a search for the willpower to keep going when it's tough.

When runners dig down for inner strength, they almost always discover it. Embedded in our DNA is the toughness developed by ancient ancestors who faced far greater challenges than finishing or running faster in a half or full marathon. When we push ourselves a bit farther or faster than we've gone before, we engage circuits that are hardwired into our being that keep us going.

But there are also circuits that try to protect us from pushing too far. The subconscious brain monitors stress buildup. When the level is determined to be too high, the reflex triggers anxiety hormones that cause one to question whether to keep exerting at that level. As the stress continues to increase, negative attitude peptides are stimulated by this subconscious brain.

Through a series of training components, you can train yourself to deal with stress in several specific areas:

- Long runs push back endurance

- Speed training pushes back stress due to running faster for a longer distance

- Form drills get one ready to shift into a smoother running gait when needed

- Mental training allows one the willpower to keep going even when stressed

Over 4-6 months, you will gradually build up the workload, allowing your body to adapt to increased performance. During a series of workouts, you gradually push beyond what you have been able to do currently. All of the workouts, with backup information, are detailed in *Year Round Plan, Half Marathon, 5K/10K,* and *Galloway Training Programs*.

There is always a risk when picking up the speed. By carefully monitoring your weak links, as noted in the book *Running Injuries – Care & Prevention*, there are few aches/pains/injuries. The greatest risk is that of failing. There are almost always workouts when the runner doesn't know whether he or she can finish it.

By making adaptations and learning how to keep going, the frontal lobe goes into action. The left side solves problems. The right side looks for sources of internal strength to keep going. They almost always find what you need.

Because you are in the human, conscious brain, you can gain control over the negative hormone production from the subconscious brain. You discover how you can overcome anxiety and doubt and be what you could be . . . on that day.

For more mental techniques and information, see *Mental Training for Runners*, available at www.jeffgalloway.com

© Creatas/Thinkstock

83 Not being afraid to fail

Just when our ego is running at an all-time high, running experiences bring us back to earth, literally. You can expect for the ego to project continuous progress during a training program – no performance is good enough, you can do better (says the ego).

When we want to run faster, the ego will help us push toward the goal, but it must be managed. When our performances don't equal the ego's projection, we are presented with one of the greatest opportunities among all growth experiences: to learn from our mistakes.

All of us are capable of extraordinary accomplishments in running and in life. To achieve a level that is "on the edge" of our experience, we must take on the risk of failure. Some cannot handle this and back off without ever testing themselves. They cut themselves off from finding hidden strengths inside, which are almost always found. The other loss is that from the exhilaration of attempting a significant challenge – even when not achieved.

I don't know of any successful person who has not failed. It is in the evaluation of a disappointing run that we question everything: goal, training, pacing, strategy, mental toughness. This activates the frontal lobe to start searching. It may not find the answers right away, but it usually does as the weeks and the workouts continue to reveal issues.

The training journey takes us through a series of gentle risks, usually balanced by gentle successes. This allows for continuous adjustments to avoid each setback in the future. One of the most important learning issues is determining how much we want to improve. Failure is often measured as the difference in our projected goal between the ego and our conscious brain in the frontal lobe. When egos tell us that we have not run as fast as we should, evaluate!

Spend 1-3 days figuring out what you could have done better. In most cases, you will have several items. Project ahead to the next workout/race and make the adjustments to improve your performance. Once you have learned from your setback, move on to the next goal.

Doubts do not mean that you don't have the confidence to achieve a goal. They spring from the stress of a workout plan that gears you to higher performance and the pressure of the goal itself. As the stress level rises, the reflex brain triggers hormones that leave you anxious and doubtful.

Embracing the fact that we may not succeed is a breakthrough. At this point, success is often produced by not giving up and continuing to run even when you doubt that you can keep going. We have many circuits in our brains that connect us with resources to keep going when we don't know what is going to happen. The more often we use them, the better we adapt our mind-body organism to realizing its potential on a given day.

It is the fear of failure that is more likely to keep us from our goal, not the act of failure. Such fears trigger negative hormones reducing motivation and reducing capacity of certain key circuits in the brain.

Taking action produces positive hormones. Set up a plan of training and action. This will get you into the frontal lobe instead of the subconscious reflex brain that responds to stress. As you fine-tune the plan and believe in it, you continue the flow of positive hormones.

The magic mile (MM) is crucial to the strategy. This will predict your current potential. It is OK to project a 3%-5% improvement during a season of training. Use the cognitive training methods in my book *Mental Training for Runners* to prepare you for the effort.

The MM gives you a glimpse into the future. If you don't achieve your goal on the first try, you can learn from your mistakes and go for it again.

Making adaptations as you go helps you become a smarter, faster and better runner – if you're not afraid to fail.

84 To deal with challenges

There is something exhilarating in overcoming a challenge and going on to finish a race or workout. Once you do this a few times, you'll develop the confidence to confront future issues. You're also setting up a circuit that can be used to deal with challenges in other areas of life. It may surprise you, but the best way to get through a challenge may not be pushing harder.

Make sure your goal is realistic. Use the MM time trial (page 139). This will help you avoid the frustration of running at a race pace that you are currently not ready to run.

Don't give up. The single reason why some runners succeed and others don't is that the winners don't give up, nor do they neglect training because of setbacks. Learn from mistakes and keep trying.

© altrendo images/Stockbyte/Thinkstock

Save resources! When a physical challenge occurs during the early or middle portions of a hard effort, it's a sign that some of your resources are not ready for the challenge at that moment. Ease off the effort for a minute or so and then gradually ease back to the point that feels do-able during that workout or race.

During workouts, you can push the middle section of each fast segment. When you're running a one mile repeat, to improve your marathon speed, run the first quarter mile and the last quarter mile at goal pace and the middle portion about 30-45 seconds per mile faster than goal pace.

Save your best effort for the end of the race. Many studies and surveys show that by conserving resources early in a distance race, one can run faster times overall. Having a strategy allows you to use the conscious brain, be "in the moment," and make the changes you need to overcome the challenge of the moment while staying on track for your goal.

As you manage your challenges, with the strategies that worked, you'll learn more with each experience.

- When to keep going at a given effort level and when to back off.

- When to continue trying and when to save the effort for another day.

- When to have a good time, and when to go for a fast time.

Mantras help!
- I can do it!

- Don't give up!

- I'm feeling better!

- I feel the strength!

- I'm feeling stronger!

- I'm running lighter!

- I'm getting closer!

- I'm feeling smoother!

- I can do it!

© Stockbyte/Thinkstock

85 Finishing a tough workout

You're into a hard workout, and you're really tired. The stress is building up in the subconscious reflex brain, triggering anxiety hormones. This is a warning sign that things could get worse, but you don't focus on the negative feelings that will stimulate negative attitude peptides.

Instead, you put yourself into neutral. You're not continuing to push harder, you simply keep going. It's OK to let the times of the speed repetitions slip a bit. At the same time, evaluate whether there is a real medical reason why you can't run the workout assigned. If there is a reason, back off and call it a day. This will get you under the control of the conscious brain and allow you a chance to recover and come back to this workout within 2-3 days.

The problem is most commonly due to not taking conscious control over your thinking during a tough workout. You are letting the reflex brain build up stress and then subconsciously trigger negative attitude hormones. To do your best in a race, you must learn how to deal with these problems in workouts. As you push through these motivational slumps, you will develop the internal resources to do so when you have even more challenges later. You will also change the chemistry inside billions of cells, sometimes within a minute or two.

By using the cognitive strategy below, you can take control over the reflex brain and significantly reduce the production of negative peptides. If you are realistic about your effort on that day and go through a positive thought process, you can stimulate the production of positive attitude hormones.

Each of us has a lot more control over our situation in a stressful workout than we think we do. By practicing the strategy below and believing in the results, you can not only finish the workout you need to prepare for your next goal, but you can access the conscious brain to retrain the reflex brain to move you into a positive mindset – even when tired and under stress.

Toughing out the workout

Focus on the next segment of the workout. Let's say that you have 4 one-mile repetitions left, and the reflex brain is monitoring a lot of stress and producing negative attitude hormones. As you finish your rest interval, you are feeling less and less like doing the rest of the workout.

Tell your conscious brain that you are going to run the first quarter of the next one. As you start to run at a pace that is OK, and you are focusing on a distance you know you can finish, positive hormones are produced, and your attitude shift begins. Passing one quarter mile, you agree to do another quarter of a mile and congratulate yourself for moving forward. Segment by segment you focus on positive thoughts, finish the mile, and feel good about completing it. More positive secretions push your mood to the positive and keep the negative emotions away.

Say positive things: "I'm pushing back my barriers." "I'm overcoming challenges." "This is making me tougher." As you add to the number of repetitions during each workout and talk to the frontal lobe, you empower it to reprogram the reflex brain and lock into a series of steps to get through the fatigue at the end of the workout. By the time you run the goal race, the reflex brain is ready to click in to one positive step at a time to get to the end.

Confront left brain feelings with strength statements: I don't quit! I can do it!
Mental toughness starts with, simply, not giving up. Just ignore the negative messages, stay focused on the next few steps, and talk to yourself. Positive affirmations activate positive peptides.

86 When you start to "lose it" in a tough race

Champions feel the same or greater discomfort as the ones behind themselves; they just hang on longer and get through it. You have it in you to play a poker game with yourself and the others behind you. Even if you feel stressed, tired and not up to the task, break up the remaining distance into segments. Focus only on the next segment.

It's possible to reverse a downward drift in motivation when under the physical and mental stress of a race. The greatest reward is an amazing sense of satisfaction from turning a negative situation into a positive one. Due to the increasing physical fatigue and pressure that you put on yourself, there will be feelings of doubt and low motivation triggered by the subconscious reflex brain. If you focus on these messages, you will produce negative attitude peptides.

- By rehearsing the negative messages you could get, you will desensitize yourself to their attitude-lowering effect.

- Confront each negative feeling with a positive statement:

The negative is . . . The positive is . . .

"Back off, this isn't your day." "Don't give up!"

"There are other races." "I can do it today!"

"Why are you doing this?" "I'm getting tougher!"

- Evaluate whether there is a real medical reason (which is rare). If there is a health problem, back off and conserve — there will be another day.

   Most commonly, the reflex brain is responding to the stress buildup of the race by triggering negative peptides, creating a negative emotional environment. A successful strategy during the first onset of this attitude downturn is to glide a little. If needed, take a short walk break (15-20 seconds) to mentally regroup and focus on the next segment of the race.

- Activate your rhythmic breathing (mentioned in the in the "Jumpstart your motivation" section, page 45. Smile and start running again with a light touch and smooth cadence. Each one of these actions engages the frontal lobe and stimulates the positive peptides to transmit a message of hope throughout the body.

- To do your best in a race, you must manage the stress buildup by using a routine such as those that follow. You are training yourself to keep going, which is 90% of the battle. You are also programming the conscious brain to regularly check on the reflex brain, stop the negative thoughts, and insert positive beliefs.

Note: None of these drills is cast in stone. Adapt them to your needs and strengths. You will continue to edit them as you move through the process.

- Confront reflex brain feelings with strength statements: Don't quit! I can do it! In your speed workouts, practice the following drill. Fine-tune this so that when you run your goal race, you will have a strategy for staying mentally focused and positive. Your belief in a plan will increase the production of positive motivational hormones.

The scene

You're getting very tired and stressed in a race, you'd really like to call it quits, or at least slow down significantly.

Quick strategies:

- Break up the remaining race into segments that you know you can do:

- "One more minute." Run for one minute, then reduce pace slightly for a few seconds, then say, "one more minute," again and again (or 30 seconds, or 15 seconds, etc.).

- "Ten more steps." Run about 10 steps, take a couple of easy steps, then say, "ten more steps."

- "One more step." Keep saying this over and over — you'll get there.

- Take an extra walk break to "gather yourself" if you need it.

- Take some gliding breaks. By doing the "acceleration-glider" drill during workouts, you will be prepared to do this in the race. See page 82.

- Reduce the tension in your leg muscles and feet by gliding for a few strides every 1-2 minutes. The acceleration-glider drill prepares you for this moment, particularly when coasting downhill.

Segment by segment

- During the workouts, if you really question your ability to finish, start each repetition, or race segment by saying to yourself, "just one more" (even if you have 4 to go) or "10 more steps." You can make it the whole way.

- Teamwork! You are needed by the team. If you're not on a team or Galloway training group, imagine that you are. The belonging to a larger group with team spirit can pull you through many difficult workouts. Even if you have a long distance friend that you are going to report to, it helps to have that connection. Some runners bring their cellphone on long runs and call their friend as a "lifeline."

- When you are getting close to the end and really feel like you can't keep going, say to yourself, "I am tough" or "I can endure" or "Yes, I can" or "One more step."

"I CAN DO IT . . . I AM DOING IT . . . I DID IT!

Note: For more information on and explanations of this, see my book Mental Training.

87 I have a secret weapon: I know my current potential

Most runners go into a race without knowing how fast they are ready to run. It's not surprising that most let their egos set a pace that is too fast. The result is a dramatic slowdown during the last portion of the race.

Knowing your current potential gives you a huge advantage. This will not only motivate you to do your best, it will bestow confidence. When you believe in what you can do, you are more likely to achieve at that level.

In our Galloway training programs, we use the "magic mile," or MM, which has been an extremely accurate predictive tool. It is based upon tens of thousands of reports and is described in the sidebar below.

© vndrpttn/iStockphoto/Thinkstock

Whether you choose the MM or another predictor, use it regularly. This allows you to set realistic goals and keeps you from exceeding your speed limit on long runs, during time goal workouts, and at the beginning of races.

The MM tracks how much one slows down when running longer events and can designate a safe pace per mile on long runs. It is inserted into a few key workouts each month as noted in the schedules in my books *5K/10K, Half Marathon, Galloway Training Programs*, and *Year Round Plan*. Just look at the weeks that have the MM listed.

Using the MM activates the frontal lobe, or the executive brain. In doing so, you gain conscious control over your training and stay focused. This "human brain" can override the subconscious reflex brain when it gets over-stressed and help to reduce negative attitude hormones. Conscious evaluation of the MM can hold back the ego projections, which are almost always too optimistic.

Look at the information below to see what your MM time predicts in your goal race. If the MM predicts a current time goal, runners are motivated to pursue this goal. You know that it is possible and that activates positive attitude hormones.

If the MM predicts a slower time than your time goal, this is a signal to "step up" the training. You will have several chances to improve, and most runners keep getting faster throughout the program. Since the MM predicts the best possible performance under ideal conditions, it's best to record an MM time that is faster than you need.

At the end of the season, take your best MM time and do the math. Add 10-30 seconds per mile to adjust for "imperfect" conditions on race day. You'll then have a realistic goal and the confidence that will help you achieve it.

The **"Magic Mile" time trials (MM)** are reality checks on your goal. These should be done on the weeks noted on the schedule. The MM has been the best predictor of current potential and helps to set a realistic training pace. With this information, you can decide how hard to run during various situations. (If you have any injuries, you should not do the MM.)

- Warm up for the MM with about 10 minutes of very easy running with liberal walk breaks.

- Do 4-6 accelerations as described in the book – no sprinting.

- Run around a track if at all possible (or a very accurately measured segment).

- Time yourself for 4 laps (or an accurately measured mile). Start the watch at the beginning, and keep it running until you cross the finish of the 4th lap.

- **On the first MM, don't run all-out: run at a pace that is only slightly faster than your current pace.**

- Only one MM is done on each day it is assigned.

- On each successive MM (usually 2-3 weeks later), your mission is to beat the previous best time.

- Don't ever push so hard that you hurt your feet, knees, etc.

- Jog slowly for the rest of the distance assigned on that day, taking as many walk breaks as you wish.

- At the end of the program, do the math listed in the next section: "Galloway's Performance Predictor"

- Training pace is at least two minutes per mile slower than predicted maximum marathon pace (MM x 1.3).

After you have run three of these MMs (not at one time but on different weekends), you'll see progress and will run them hard enough so that you are huffing and puffing during the second half. For prediction purposes, you want to finish feeling like you couldn't go much farther at that pace. Try walking for about 10-15 seconds at the half during the MM. Some runners record a faster time when taking short breaks, and some go faster when running continuously. Do what works for you.

Galloway's Performance Predictor

Step 1: Run your "magic mile" time trial (MM) (Four laps around the track)

Step 2: Compute your mile pace for the marathon by multiplying by 1.3

For the half marathon, multiply by 1.2

For the 10K, multiply by 1.15

For the 5K, add 33 seconds per mile

Note: These computations are the fastest that you could hope to achieve after having done all of the time goal training elements in my books under ideal conditions. Remember to slow the pace of races and long runs by 30 sec/mile for every 5F above 60F (20 sec/km for every 2C above 14C)

Note: When running marathons with over 10,000 participants, you will tend to run about half a mile farther than marathon distance. When the registration exceeds 30,000, the extra distance is usually over a mile. Thus, large population races are not ideal venues for running fast times.

88 To prepare for my goal

Because I have an appointment with a race on my calendar, I feel more motivated to get out and run. I choose the goal and date, so I'm in charge.

Some find a challenge in a 5K/10K. But many can bluff their way through these distances and need a half or full marathon to challenge them to do all of the training runs. The goal must be demanding enough so that the individual knows that he/she must check each workout off the schedule.

Avoid putting stress on yourself. Use the MM in the segment above this one. The magic mile is a reality check on your goal and can help you monitor progress on the way to your goal race.

After several campaigns, there is satisfaction in knowing that you are making progress – that each workout has a purpose. You are getting the job done by getting out there.

Barbara and I are currently running a marathon every month. Even after having finished over 160 marathons, I've not found any of them to be easy or routine. Our scheduled marathon each month is our goal/challenge and also serves as the last long run for the next one.

Many of my e-coaching clients find that a race of any distance, once a month, "keeps them honest" in terms of getting in the runs during the week. Not only do you want to be prepared, but the finishing of any event tends to bestow motivation for weeks afterward.

Just crossing the finish of a significant event is empowering and can change the way you look at yourself for the better. Even more powerful is the continued reinforcement of 6 months of success stories. Each training success leads you toward the race. Each finish gives a boost to the next training season.

Pick your goal

There are many goals that will help you stay focused, providing motivation to train. Here are some suggestions. Chose one or more. Enjoy the journey

- Race – Choose a distance that will motivate you to train
- Mileage – Many runners are motivated to maintain a certain weekly mileage
- "X" weeks when you have run 3 days a week – 3 days will maintain your conditioning
- To run once a week on an enjoyable trail/route
- To finish a half or full marathon in each of the 50 states
- Birthday run: To run the number of miles or kilometers as your age over 1-7 days
- To run until I'm 100 – This is my goal and why I wrote the book with that title.

89 To set my own personal record

There's a significant uplift to the spirit when we run a personal best. Most runners can accomplish this every year by using a little creativity.

Among my e-coach clients who have done the work necessary to improve, most have continued for at least 10 years from the time they started running. The prime reason for success tends to be focusing on the key factors that provide the maximum improvement, such as increasing the long run and targeted speed sessions.

Staying injury-free is another crucial element. I've sustained an injury-free streak of over 30 years by following the tips in *Running Injuries – Care/Prevention*. I have heard from many other runners who have avoided injuries for decades by following the principles in this book.

Mature runners who have reached a peak and/or don't want to do speedwork can pick a distance that they have not run before. Have fun with this. For example, if your birthday is January 11, measure an 11-mile course or an 11km course and run it for time. You may set a world record for some distances. Some push back their endurance record by running one mile (or one kilometer) farther on their birthday week each year.

It helps to challenge a friend when running these distance or time records. Set up a goal date for setting the record and enjoy some "trash talk" as you go through the training.

Categories for setting records

- Birthday record: Run a mile or a kilometer farther during the week of your birthday

- Run more days per year than before

- Increase the average mileage per day

- Set up your own world record distance (1.11 kilometers)

- Laps covered around a track

- Set up your own category

- Have your "world record" list on the wall

Example: World record for pi: 3.1416 miles or kilometers

© Vernon Wiley/iStockphoto/Thinkstock

90 To break through previous distance barriers

One of the greatest feelings of empowerment in life comes from going farther than you have run in the last month or so. Pushing back the endurance barrier signals your mind-body that you are improving and you're getting better.

If you run slowly and insert frequent walk breaks, there are many physiological enhancements that occur during a series of gradually increasing long runs.

- Heart function increases

- Blood circulation is improved

- Capillaries increase in the exercising muscles

- Fat burning capacity is enhanced

- Running form tends to be more efficient

- Mental toughness increases as you keep pushing past the recent longest run

- Stamina to endure other fatigue experiences is improved

Embedded in the human DNA is the ability to adapt to going farther because this allowed our ancient ancestors to survive. For most of our existence as human beings, food was scarce and covering 10-20 miles a day increased the potential for accumulating the needed calories.

Extending our current distance frontier revs up our performance and triggers circuits that make adaptations in the various body parts and organs. The feet move more efficiently, reducing effort and aggravation. Oxygen absorption increases. The energy system goes into conservation mode. The central nervous system steps up when you go farther, activating body and mind to get the job done.

Some of the most powerful positive attitude hormones are produced when we're tired and continue to move forward. These "attitude boosters" lock into billions of receptors throughout the mind-body network delivering positive and confident feelings.

Running slower on long runs does not detract from the endurance, accomplishment, or sense of empowerment. Walking more frequently reduces the fatigue without taking away the satisfaction in achievement.

Because you're solving problems along the way, brain control tends to shift into the frontal lobe. This control center overrides the subconscious brain, managing stress and lowering the production of negative attitude or anxiety hormones.

Frontal lobe thinking keeps you in the moment. You're open to what is coming next, ready to adapt. The left side deals with logical issues and problem solving. The right side offers creative solutions and intuitive connections to hidden sources of strength.

Slow down and enjoy the exhilaration of going farther.

Increasing the long run safely

1. Start with a distance that is only 1-2 miles farther than your longest run in the past two weeks.

2. Slow down the pace as indicated by the magic mile (page 139).

3. Insert liberal walk breaks from the beginning.

4. Follow a structured plan of increase.

5. It helps to have a goal race.

6. Don't be afraid to slow down more.

7. Adjust for heat – 30 sec/mi slower with each 5F increase in temperature (20 sec/KM slower with each 2C increase in temperature).

Note: For specific training schedules see my books *5K/10K, Half Marathon, Year Round Plan*, and *Galloway Training Programs* available at www.jeffgalloway.com

91 I want to feel the wind on my face

There's something exhilarating about being able to pick up the pace and feel like you're running fast. Your mind-body organism increases capacity, expands awareness, and activates many components that aren't normally "on alert."

Actual speed doesn't matter. What used to be my slowest pace, when I was on the Olympic team, is now my fastest pace. By picking up the speed during a run, even for a short segment, I feel more alive throughout my body. The term I use for these faster segments is "accelerations."

The distance of this acceleration does not have to be more than 10 to 20 steps. At first, it should be only 10 steps to warm up the legs, followed by easing back to a jog for 20-30 steps. I follow the "Caution – Speed Zone" suggestions below and have not been injured in over 30 years. The gentle warm-up is crucial to acquiring a faster speed.

I enjoy the challenge of working through the various paces as I speed up. I feel the body respond to exertion with more energy and more vitality with mental alertness. Even a few small segments of increase will leave me feeling better after the run.

The actual amount of time run at the fast pace is not very long most of the time. I will usually pick up the pace, ease off, jog, and then repeat the cycle. The "acceleration-glider" drill is my most common format. See the segment on page 82.

Once I've achieved my current fast speed, it is exhilarating to feel the wind on my face, to know that I can still pick it up and use my feet and legs to go faster. I don't run nearly as fast as I did 40 years ago, but I feel as good as ever when I run fast. You can, too!

Caution – Speed zone

1. Running faster increases the chance of injury.

2. Never run at top speed (don't sprint).

3. Warm up gently and thoroughly.

4. Run faster for only a few steps on the first speed segment.

5. Glide back down to an easy pace so that there is no huffing and puffing.

6. Gradually pick up the pace again, going a few steps farther.

7. Do as many of these segments as you wish.

8. Never suddenly increase the speed or distance of the fast segment.

9. Enjoy the feeling of moving fast again.

92 To push my limits

Some of my real "breakthrough" moments in life, when I really got to know myself, occurred during workouts when I doubted my ability to finish. There's something about the combination of stresses during an endurance challenge that can tap into a powerful combination of previously unused inner reserves.

Life stress and the demands of exertion can trigger the secretion of negative attitude hormones, reducing blood flow to key areas by the subconscious brain. As we push on during difficult workouts, negative attitude hormones are also subconsciously secreted, reducing motivation. Most average citizens back off or stop the workout and never know what they are capable of doing.

By taking positive mental action, we gain control over our attitude, lower the stress, reduce production of the negative hormones, and can stimulate the production of positive hormones. The simple way to do this is to have a cognitive strategy, such as the one suggested below. This allows you to make changes at any point during the workout. When focusing on logical strategy, brain control shifts to the frontal lobe, which can override the stress reactions of the subconscious reflex brain.

The human organism is designed to rebuild stronger after a significant stress. The best plan for pushing the limits is to schedule a series of workouts, with sufficient recovery afterward, that gradually increase the number of segments of faster-paced running. With each gentle increase, one receives a sense of accomplishment. The repair period afterward does not mean that you have to lie down. Appropriate cross training is allowed. The reduction in intensity will vary among individuals, but usually two or three easy days per week are needed for repair and rebuilding.

Training ourselves to go a little farther when under duress develops the awareness and capability to push on when you don't feel good. The personal empowerment in breaking through past barriers keeps on giving. I've heard from thousands who applied this mental enhancement process to other areas in life: career, family, personal, etc.

Embedded in our DNA is the intuitive ability to activate embedded circuits that keep us going when under stress. During these challenges, we discover that there's a lot more in our inner resource tank than we thought.

That's empowering in itself.

Strategy for pushing back the barriers

- Ensure that there is not a medical reason for not continuing (uncommon)
- Set up a training program that you look at regularly
- Schedule small increases during each "challenge" workout
- Include a rest/repair period after pushing ahead
- Be sure to run about every other day to maintain adaptations
- Use the mental training techniques in my book *Mental Training*

93 I love pushing back the speed barriers

Increasing the number of repetitions during a speed training program bestows a unique sense of achievement. You are not only pushing back the distance, but with each workout you monitor pacing, form, and weak links – making constant adjustments.

The greatest stress, and the source of the greatest improvement, is incurred as one continues to keep going when tired at the end of these workouts. Internal improvements are constantly made in physiology, form, and mental tenacity.

In practically every speed workout, one will reach a point when finishing doesn't seem possible. Each person must discover her own way of getting through these rough patches. The common factors to get to the finish are first, "don't give up." The second step is to simply put one foot in front of another and keep moving.

I've had hundreds of speed workouts when I didn't feel good at any time during the workout. Some of these were superb workouts. The exhilaration in finishing is immense. On those days, you just have to get out there and do it. You learn that the way you feel, body and mind, doesn't often indicate how you can perform on that day.

Because one must overcome a number of challenges, finishing a speed workout can bestow several layers of satisfaction at once.

Pushing the speed barriers

1. Be realistic.

2. Monitor weak links.

3. Don't increase more than is listed in the schedules of my books listed below.

4. Stop the workout at the first sign of an injury.

5. Take more rest if needed.

6. First and last repetitions are a bit slower.

7. Schedule in your journal.

8. Read the past workout entries before starting the next one.

Resources: *5K/10K, Half Marathon, Year Round Plan, Galloway Training Programs*

Chapter 11
To have fun

94 To run with a friend

I've had my best laughs (and my most honest discussions) during my runs. I look forward to each run with my friends for I know that I'll learn some new information, enjoy smiling and laughing, feel support without having to ask for it, and sometimes solve the world's problems.

Some runners will choose a running companion, on a given day, based upon how they are feeling. It might be someone who tells jokes (they don't have to be good). Many runners conduct project discussions during a run with a resource person for a current operation. Someone who tells good and long stories is a wonderful companion for long runs.

There's a special chemistry between running friends that invites joking, open discussion, true confessions and often a secret or two. Most runners become

more guttural during a run and often divulge information that is normally not disclosed in other environments. This probably evolved during the continuous treks that our ancient ancestors made in small groups.

Their trust and confidence in one another enhanced survival. Today our disclosures make the runs more interesting as the miles go by.

Our Galloway training groups are divided into pace groups with the mission that all runners stay together for the length of the run. To stimulate conversation in the beginning or when tired, many of our group leaders ask the members to bring three things with them: a joke, a juicy story, and a political issue.

After a good friendship run, the mind is spinning with the personal details, disclosures, stories, personality impact, and smiles. The connection with your friend renews the wonderful sense of connection, with each looking forward to the next time together.

95 To write my novel

You can turn a boring run into a fun experience by writing a chapter of your novel during your run. Each street, trail, block, store, house is loaded with stories. As you run by, let the right brain unlock these stories.

The creative right side of the frontal lobe is engaged when we run. This can allow us to solve problems, activate a design, paint a portrait, and write another chapter. The use of this component keeps us in the moment, allowing for new thoughts to erupt regularly, whether they are logical or not. Many famous artists (musicians, actors, architects) have said that running is a significant stimulus to their creativity.

© iStockphoto/Thinkstock

Each of us is producing a novel as we live our life. We may never write it down, but we move from one episode to the next. Running allows us a chance to reflect upon the "chapters," make them come alive, and enhance the characters or details.

I've known several runners who actually have written a novel based upon material generated during a series of runs. Some of these were bizarre and others followed life experiences or had a running theme. Many other runners, however, let their right brain imagination take off as they weave a plot, mold a character, fill in details, etc. It helps to have a friend who is working on the novel with you. All of us, however, are capable of bringing out our creative side and having fun doing so.

As soon as you return from the run, jot down a few of the ideas generated. Most use their journal or have a file on their computer. Before you go out for the next run, read over what you wrote down before.

You will probably be surprised with some of the material. Who knows, it might be the next cult running novel.

96 To win my Olympic medal

Fantasy sports are popular today. During your runs, you can construct a fantasy running world and have fun. During these imaginative journeys, you can run some incredible workouts, come from behind to win the Olympic gold medal, or set the world record. Some runners enjoy imagining running with a friend who is far away. Others will run with a legendary runner and help him or her win a key race. If you don't have a chance to qualify for the Olympics, you can pick your favorite Olympiad and go for the gold.

Set the scene. Pick one of the situations below or choose one of your own. Some find motivation in writing down the scene before they run. Others will read a novel or a historical book before starting and then try to relive or change the outcome of a race.

Pick interesting characters. You can either use real people or make up your own companions/competitors. Include a mix of people from your neighborhood and those on the top 10 world list.

Plot line: During each run, construct the plot. Some have an outcome in mind at the start. Others like to let the plot evolve. Have fun with this.

Do research: If you have been inspired by runners in the past (such as those listed in this book) reenact the famous races. As you research the heroes, their competitors and the race situation, you'll learn and be inspired.

Become a sportscaster: Talk yourself through a "play-by-play" during the run. You could play both the announcer and the competitor.

Set up your fantasy record book: Those who have a race or two that they enjoy revisiting will sometimes have a "record book" on the wall where they record the time or distance run.

Fantasy running

- Running with a friend or family member – working out a problem
- Running with a legend
- Winning a big race
- Setting a world record
- Sharing a run with someone you admire

© Ryan McVay/Digital Vision/Thinkstock

Chapter 12
To gain control over my weight

97 Do I run to eat or eat to run?

We've targeted one of the basic philosophical issues of running. Whatever side you choose, on any given day, you can win both ways if you set up a strategy. Food offers the energy we need for running and the timing of food intake can improve or detract from your workouts. Gentle, aerobic running will stimulate appetite, but it will also trigger the burning of fat. Here's how it works.

Our subconscious brain has many behavioral eating patterns that were set up more than a million years ago. Long before our ancestors discovered how to use tools or to strategically hunt, they survived by moving constantly and gathering bits of food. Starvation was common. Our digestive tracts are set up to store potential energy in the form of fat when food is available by significantly delaying the production of hormones that leave one feeling satisfied after big meals. Our reflex brain makes sure that we have enough reserve fuel on board for extended periods of starvation. However, it does its job too well.

Our bodies were designed to exercise and work better in every area when we get our daily exertion. Those who are under a high level of stress find that a correctly paced workout reduces stress. But when we don't move around and burn enough calories, the stress builds up and triggers a number of negative subconscious behavior patterns.

Surprisingly, scientists have found that when we don't burn the minimum calories we are programmed to burn, our appetite is stimulated and we tend to get into a pattern of reflex eating that triggers a powerful neurotransmitter, dopamine. Research shows that very sedentary people eat more than very active people, and they feel more tired and less motivated. By moving ourselves around for a few miles a day (running or walking), we activate systems that can keep appetite and energy in balance.

There's an excellent sourcebook by Robert Portman and John Ivy called *Hardwired for Fitness*. It shows how the various circuits in your reflex subconscious brain function and how you can work in harmony with your needs.

For 30-40 minutes after a run, you turn on a switch in your brain that can maximize the reloading the glycogen used during the run. Eating a snack of 100-300 calories, composed of 80% simple carbohydrates (sugar) and 20% protein, will help reload the muscles.

Tools that can help you shift away from the reflex brain

(From my book *Mental Training for Runners*)

- Use a website like www.fitday.com to monitor intake and analyze nutrition.
- Use a resource like *A Woman's Guide to Fatburning* by Barbara and Jeff Galloway for backup information and to understand the process.
- Set your calorie deficit goal each day (150 is the maximum recommended)
- Set up a calorie "budget" for each day
- Get a step counter and increase the number of walking steps to achieve your calorie deficit (10,000 is the goal)
- As you monitor your eating and exercise, you can take action to improve the efficiency of the process. You control your budget.
- Increasing walking steps can allow you to have a calorie deficit while eating as many calories as before.

How to modify reflex eating behaviors

- Write down everything you eat.
- Estimate calorie content before eating anything – this shifts consciousness to frontal lobe.
- If there are foods that you really love, which are hazardous to your diet, eat small amounts and account for these snacks.
- Search for foods that are healthy to take the place of the unhealthy foods.
- Reward yourself for making progress with a pair of shoes, etc.

98 I run to control my food intake

We have many circuits inside the brain that trigger eating behaviors. If we don't burn a certain threshold of calories each day, the hunger circuit is stimulated.

In the book *Hardwired for Fitness*, Drs. Portman and Ivy document how our brain monitors calorie burning. Surprisingly, regular physical activity helps to control appetite while sedentary behavior stimulates appetite. So if you want to keep from being hungry much of the time, keep moving. As noted in the sidebar below, reaching a threshold of calories burned each day coordinated the circuits that control hunger and energy.

Running gently, with walk breaks, is a great way to rev up your calorie burning. But if you run too hard, a significant amount of glycogen will be used. This storage form of carbohydrate is the brain's reserve fuel source. If it is not replaced within 30 minutes of finishing a run, there will be some appetite increase.

The glycogen reloading switches are "on" within the first 30 minutes after finishing a run. Eating a reloading meal, as noted below, can reduce the hunger response.

Walking is another great way to burn the calories while reducing hunger. Little if any glycogen is burned when walking, reducing the hunger. The more steps taken, the more fat burned. You can insert segments of walking during sedentary periods of the day. This improves health while burning fat.

Reducing hunger through exercise

1. Burning a threshold of calories brings hunger and exercise into balance. See note below**

2. Walking burns fat and reduces hunger response

3. Running easily with walk breaks maximizes fat burning, but there will be some hunger

4. Reduce hunger by eating a reloading meal:
   - Within 30 minutes of finishing
   - 80% simple carbs/20% protein
   - 100-300 calories
   - Accelerade/Endurox, have 80/20 in the mix.

**@700 calories for a 150 lb person, @1000 for someone weighing 200 lbs (from *Hardwired for Fitness* by Robert Portman and John Ivy).

© Hemera/Thinkstock

99 I run so that I can burn off some fat

Running is one of the best ways to burn fat and transform your muscle cells into fat burners over a 1-2 year period. By combining gentle running with purposeful eating and gentle walking, it's possible to produce more lean body mass as you lower the fat percentage.

But many beginners get discouraged after the first few months because they don't see a major drop in body weight. As your body adapts from sedentary life to endurance running, body weight (not fat) may temporarily increase with the addition of more blood plasma and greater storage of glycogen for energy. With every gram of additional glycogen, the body stores 4 grams of water. It is common for a runner to add 5-7 pounds so that the body can perform better physiologically.

The key training factors that promote fat burning are the following:

1. Running a slow long run each week (with walk breaks) of at least 90 minutes.

2. Running two other runs of at least 60 minutes per week.

3. Walking a total of at least 10,000 steps a day.

4. Insertion of liberal walk breaks into every run.

To burn fat, you must exercise aerobically. This means going at a slow enough pace so that the muscles are getting an adequate supply of oxygen, with no huffing and puffing.

When you run too fast, the muscles cannot get enough oxygen to burn fat and will shift to burning glycogen. This produces a high waste product, tight muscles as the workout continues, and significant huffing and puffing.

But if you don't exercise control over the income side of the equation, weight will not be lost. There are several key factors that my wife Barbara has noted in our book *A Woman's Guide to Running/Fatburning*. By conducting your eating behaviors in your frontal lobe, you can gain conscious control and burn it off!

Eating with a purpose

*   Write down everything you eat

*   Know the calorie content and nutrient breakdown of what you're eating (read the label or use a website like www.fitday.com)

*   Concentrate on the positive: "I can eat more of (good tasting fruit and crunchy vegetables)" rather than "I have to eat less of _____"

*   Visualize the food on your plate as being in your stomach. Ask yourself, "Do I want to stretch my stomach to cram in more food" or "Do I need that much right now?"

*   Don't have more than 3 items or "dishes" at one meal

*   Use spices to improve the taste of food. Food that is "spicy" tends to leave you feeling more satisfied

*   Drink a glass of water (6-8oz) before eating, and drink 4-6 oz during the meal

- Hot fluids (tea, coffee, broth) leave you feeling fuller than cold fluids

- Never eat fatty appetizers if you are very hungry before a meal. Instead, choose soup, salad, hot tea, warm skim milk.

- Take vitamins with a meal and avoid caffeine for half an hour

- Don't even think about going to a buffet

- Visit the grocery store with a mission. Have a list of exactly what you will buy and only buy what is on the list. This keeps you in the conscious brain.

- Eat more vegetables that are grilled or baked (without oil) or stir-fried, or eat them raw or in salads

- Use non-fat dressings or spray-on dressings for salads

- Eat slowly! Increase the number of chews for each bite; this triggers more satisfaction in the stomach.

- Count every calorie eaten. It only hurts you to "forget" the amount or certain foods in your totals

- Fluid calories add up quickly. Budget your alcohol, fruit juice, etc.

- Buy the highest quality foods: lean meats, fruits, veggies and whole grain products. These may cost a little more, but you'll appreciate the quality, especially when the taste is better. You will feel better about the quality of your nutrition.

- Herbs and spices can enhance the savory flavor of foods, leaving you satisfied with fewer calories consumed.

- Try to accumulate your daily quota of vitamins and minerals from food. If your daily analysis of nutrients shows regular deficiencies (based upon the recommended daily allowance, RDA) then find a really good vitamin. Jeff travels a lot and takes Cooper Complete vitamins, designed by Dr. Kenneth Cooper.

- In choosing a restaurant, check out the websites to find one that breaks down the nutritional composition of the menu items. By planning ahead, you can avoid impulse eating.

- Another option is to get a nutritional guide when you arrive at the restaurant and analyze it before the waiter takes your order

- Try to avoid or severely limit trans fats and saturated fat.

100 I run to cut down on reflex eating

Drs Portman and Ivy *(Hardwired for Fitness)* also explain how our appetite circuits were developed millions of years ago as our ancient ancestors developed coping mechanisms when food supply was constantly scarce.

A survival circuit evolved that kept the "feeling full" circuits from being activated long after our Paleolithic relatives had gorged themselves. The reflex brain kept triggering an subconscious eating pattern.

But this lack of feeling full enabled the ancients to survive. Those who ate large quantities when food was available established a fat reserve that kept them alive during periods of starvation. We have inherited this circuitry.

© More Pixels/iStockphoto/Thinkstock

The simple act of writing down everything we eat has been shown to significantly reduce excess calories and calories from unhealthy food. This logging process gets you into the conscious brain so that you can control your eating activity.

Otherwise, we tend to respond to reflex eating behaviors based upon taste. Junk food makers know that combinations of sugar, salt, and fat can stimulate a powerful neurotransmitter called dopamine. This produces a substantial pleasure effect, and the subconscious brain triggers a reflex eating pattern. There's no accountability. You can eat 20 potato chips or 200 without realizing how many.

Write it down

Account for it

Put it in your budget

Setting up a calorie budget

by Barbara Galloway

Everyone has to deal with a budget of some type. A daily calorie budget will allow you to have your chocolate while working on nutrition and fat-burning goals if you wish. Running not only increases your calorie budget for the day, it can burn more calories in a shorter period of time.

By setting up your budget, you activate your frontal lobe and take conscious control over your eating. By writing down what you eat you can stay in the conscious brain and avoid subconscious reflex eating. By analyzing your actions at the end of the day you'll understand where the calories are coming from and can arrange for an allotment for your chocolate "cravings."

True confessions: It is initially frustrating to write everything down and then to enter it into the website or notebook at the end of the day. You will get used to this. Within two weeks, most women realize that this is the most important part of calorie management. Knowledge can give you power over food intake, and journaling is a great tool to gain control.

Most women we've known who cannot control their weight don't use a journal. Once you go through the analysis for a few weeks, you can look at a food on a shelf or in a menu and guess very accurately the calorie content and the breakdown of many nutrients. You may still eat some or all of the food, but you'll know what you're doing.

- Buy a journal: Carry it everywhere, and write down everything you eat! Go to an office supply store or a bookstore and find a journal format that you like, fits into your purse, etc.

- When you eat or drink anything (including water), quickly write down the food eaten before or immediately after consuming it.

- At first, you may need to measure items with a food scale, measuring spoons, and cups. Learn portion sizes of your favorite foods. Hint, a "portion" is about the size of your fist or a deck of playing cards.

- **Using a journal activates the conscious brain, allowing you to analyze and control your eating.**

When eating in restaurants:
- Go to restaurants where there is a chart or brochure on the nutritional breakdown of the food served.

- In a restaurant, ask if they have a recipe notebook, or nutritional breakdown on their website or in the restaurant.

© Stockbyte/Thinkstock

- When buying ready-to-eat foods in a food store, look at the label.

- Some recipe books will give you an analysis of calorie breakdown and nutrients.

- Many websites have standard items (even fast food) broken down in a calorie-counting program. So you can just enter "1 Taco Bell bean burrito, fresco style" and it will do the accounting for you.

Hint: When you suspect (or realize) that a menu item will put you over the limit, get a "to go" container. When your meal is delivered, immediately put half in the container.

Set an appointment with yourself at the end of the day, to spend the time necessary to enter items consumed into your website or food log. If you wait two or three days to enter the items, you'll often forget correct quantities or inadvertently leave out items.

Simple is better. Jot down the food so that you can quickly enter the data in your computer program or food log in the evening. It helps to keep a running estimate of total calories consumed to that point in the day. Just estimate. By going through the data entry and analysis each day, you will get better and better at estimating.

Note: For more information in this area see *A Woman's Guide to Running/ Fatburning.*

Credits

Cover Design: Sabine Groten, Germany

Cover Photos: iStockphoto/Thinkstock

Photos: see individual photos

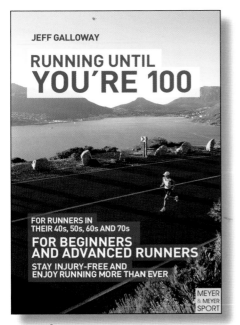
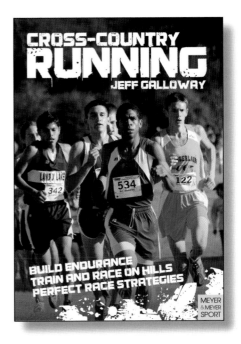